The Nurse
and
The Law

HARVEY SARNER, B.S., LL.B.

W. B. SAUNDERS COMPANY

Philadelphia · London · Toronto · 1968

W. B. Saunders Company: West Washington Square
                            Philadelphia, Pa.   19105

                            12 Dyott Street
                            London W.C. 1

                            1835 Yonge Street
                            Toronto 7, Ontario

The Nurse and the Law

Preface

The picture of the devoted nurse providing humanitarian services for her patients, oblivious to the rest of the world around her, has faded, if in fact it ever did exist except in the minds of folk hero creators. The scientist has found that he cannot devote his every waking hour to his research project and the physician has learned that there is much more to medicine and the conduct of a professional practice than providing professional services to persons in need. The nurse is just beginning to learn the same facts.

The complexities of modern life do not spare the nurse from the paperwork and other seemingly nonproductive responsibilities that modern society imposes upon her. If the nurse provides her professional services during every hour not devoted to sleep or recreation, she will find herself in the uncomfortable position of having her legal, financial, and economic affairs in a state of chaos. This is not to suggest that the nurse should devote a disproportionate amount of time to these "business" problems, thereby sacrificing time that should be devoted to her professional responsibilities.

It may seem to some that if the nurse exhibits any interest in matters of law, business, economics, insurance, finance, taxes, and so forth, she dishonors her professional commitment. Nothing can be further from the truth. The nurse has a responsibility to herself to adequately handle her business and financial affairs so that they do not become problems. If these subjects are ignored they are apt to cause such concern to the nurse that she cannot keep them out of her mind when she should be concerning herself with her patients. It is suggested that there can be a proper balance of interest and disinterest in matters of business and economics, and that the nurse can devote enough time to these matters so that they do not become problems, but not so much time that they become her preoccupation.

The medical and dental professions have learned that it is not unethical or immoral for the doctor to give some serious consideration to his business affairs, and that this need not distract from his rendering competent professional service. There is nothing in the concept of professionalism that prohibits an individual from being a good businessman. The nursing profession is just beginning to learn that it has a right to concern itself with the self-interest of its members. And it is worth repeating that serving one's self-interest is not to be criticized unless it results in sacrifice of one's professional responsibilities or is done at the expense of another. It is suggested here that the nurse can devote a proper amount of time to these subjects as they are covered in this book and serve her own self-interest without any detrimental or undesirable results. There is little or no need to warn nurses, as there is little or no need to warn doctors, that the nurse should not become preoccupied with these subjects to the level of making them her primary interest—nursing must still be her primary interest.

Each chapter of this book attempts to explain in the least complicated terms the salient legal and economic points, with a minimum of theory and a maximum of hard-core, relevant facts. The nurse need not be preoccupied with the questions of malpractice because statistically speaking there are a relatively small number of malpractice claims brought against nurses or against doctors and hospitals for the negligent conduct of nurses. However the nurse should be familiar with the general rules of law pertaining to professional responsibility. The chapters on malpractice contain a discussion of the common grounds for malpractice lawsuits against nurses and some recommendations for avoiding these situations. There is also some discussion of the mechanics of a malpractice claim and what the nurse can expect if she is unfortunate enough to be involved in such a claim.

Many of the chapters either directly or indirectly relate to the economics of the nursing profession. The nurse is just becoming aware of the fact that there is no disgrace in thinking about the economics of nursing practice and she is just approaching the point where she can talk about this subject. In the opinion of many this awakening has been long overdue.

The chapter on insurance is one of the most lengthy in the book, and perhaps the most useful. The nurse should have some basic understanding of her insurance needs. Too often professional people accept as fact the recommendations made by insurance agents, and reluctantly purchase insurance in the forms and amounts advised by the "experts" without a real understanding of the protection they have purchased and the costs involved.

Taxation, the second inevitable in our lifetime, is another misunderstood subject. Tax minimization is a lawful and important part of our economic life. The Internal Revenue Service announces each year that the majority of the taxpayers fail to take all their proper deductions and fail to file tax returns that result in the least amount of taxes. The subject of taxation is discussed in simple and uncomplicated language and presents a number of constructive methods for minimizing taxes.

One question arose when consideration was being given to the preparation of this volume. Could a book be written that would be equally applicable to the registered nurse and the practical nurse? The question was answered in the affirmative since the differences were found to be of degree and not of basic distinctions of any legal nature, except of course for the chapter on nursing practice acts, in which the legal differences between the professional and the practical nurse are discussed. Admittedly the direct audience of this small volume is the registered or the professional nurse, but there is no reason why the book cannot be equally helpful to the practical nurse and in some instances even to the volunteer or the nurse's aide. Whenever the book refers to the professional nurse, the practical nurse can easily make the transition except when it is specifically stated that the principle being discussed applies to one and not the other.

The greater portion of this book is equally applicable to the Canadian nurse. The provincial nursing practice acts are similar to the state practice acts, and there is no greater distinction between a provincial practice act and a state practice act than there is between one state law and the law of another state. It will be noted that in many instances references are made to Canadian court cases interchangeably with United States court decisions. The differences between Canadian and United States law are grossly exaggerated. In the discussion of common law, or judge-made law, especially as it pertains to professional responsibility or the malpractice, Canadian court decisions are virtually the same as the decisions of courts in the United States. Practically speaking, when attorneys prepare their briefs in malpractice cases they cite whatever favorable decisions they can find as long as they come from an English-speaking or common law country. Canadian cases are often cited in United States courts, and I am confident that the converse is equally true.

Perhaps the greatest distinction between the Canadian and United States Law pertains to the chapter on taxation. But here too, there is a gross similarity, although there is obviously a different law controlling the tax obligations of nurses in the United States and Canada. For a better understanding of the Canadian situation a short report in the *Nursing Clinics of North America* is recommended. I refer to the chapter "Law and the Nurse: The Canadian Position," by Julian D. Payne, appearing in the March 1967 *Clinics*, page 161.

Acknowledgments are in order to those who have assisted in the preparation of this book. I hesitate to start listing names for fear of omitting someone who has made a contribution. For this reason I prefer to acknowledge in a generic fashion those who assisted: my family, my secretarial staff, those nurses and others who read and corrected manuscript, and those at the W. B. Saunders Company who suggested the preparation of this book.

Harvey Sarner
Chicago, Illinois

Contents

1 *Understanding Law*

Too often an individual's only exposure to the law is in appearing before a justice of the peace to pay a traffic fine, or in seeing the newspaper account of a sensational murder trial. The law is invisible to most people, and it is only those phases of the law outside the mainstream that attract public attention. As a responsible individual the nurse should have a basic understanding of the legal system under which she lives, and she should become familiar with the particular legal rights and responsibilities that accrue to her because she is a nurse.

The legal systems of the United States and Canada are outgrowths of the English common law system, but they have reached a point of development, mainly because of size and geography, that makes comparison of their legal systems easier than comparing either one with that of Great Britain. There are some basic principles of law, equally applicable to the United States and Canada, that must be comprehended in order to understand the legal systems of these countries: They are democratic countries, federated countries, and common law countries. Each of these general principles will be described and then discussed as it relates to the nurse.

Democracy

It may seem hackneyed or trite to say that the United States and Canada are free and democratic countries. However the importance of this fact becomes evident when it is realized that only within the past 200 years was there any real acknowledgment of the fact that each man had certain natural rights, and that these rights were not subservient to the rights of a monarch or the landed gentry. Two hundred and fifty years ago it would have been radical to suggest that the peasant was on the farm for any reason other than to satisfy the whims of the landowner, and it was unheard of for the peasant to upgrade himself in order to become a member of one of the higher classes.

1

The Magna Carta, the great liberating act of 1215 granted by King John of England, established the principle that there were some human rights that superseded the rights of the king, and this established to some degree the idea that there could be a constitution above the monarch. However, this lofty principle was established only for the noblemen. It provided no benefit for the peasant, or for anyone other than the aristocrat. It was an agreement between the king and his aristocrats and not a contract between the king and all of his subjects.

It was not until the American and French Revolutions of the late eighteenth century that the principle was established that the common man had some inherent rights that superseded the rights of the king and the government. As recently as the middle part of the twentieth century the rights of the individual against the leaders of the state were tested and the question was raised whether the state was created to serve the individual or whether the individual was created to serve the state.

The United States and Canada are both constitutional as well as democratic countries. A constitution can be described as a contract between a people and their government. It insures that the basic and inherent rights of man will not be subordinated to the whim or caprice of the leaders of the nation. A country can be a democratic country without a constitution, but it is desirable that a country have a constitution to provide protection against the actions of those in legislative and executive power. The Constitution of the United States provides for a balance of power between the legislative, the executive and the judicial branches of our government by means of a system of checks and balances. It is a tribute to the framers of the Constitution that this system of checks and balances still prevails 200 years later. The legislative branch, the Congress, has powers that are not unlimited, because even the Congress is not free to violate the Constitution. The Constitution is interpreted by the Supreme Court, but even the Supreme Court is not free to violate the Constitution, and it cannot act in contradiction of statutes enacted by the Congress that do not violate the Constitution. The administrative branch, namely the President, is not free to violate the edicts of Congress or the Constitution.

The fact that she lives in a democratic country that has a constitution is of great importance to the nurse as a nurse and as a citizen. The law protects her against the arbitrary whims of the leaders of her country. The law is as certain as possible and she can rely on it for the protection of all her legal rights. This does not mean that bad laws do not exist, but these laws can be changed through the democratic process, so that the individual and the nation will benefit and not just the leaders.

Federation

The United States operates under a federated system in which the states are united under one central government. Each state, however, retains control of its own internal affairs. The state governments have enacted their own constitutions and have three branches of government which act in a manner similar to those at the national level. Each state has legislative, executive, and judicial branches, and a system of checks and balances. At the state level the executive branch is the governor, the legislative branch is the state legislature, and the judicial branch is the state supreme court.

The Constitution of the federal government provides for the police power of the states, which permits each state to engage in a large amount of self-regulation. The Constitution also provides that those powers and authorities not specifically delegated to the state governments shall be reserved for the federal government.

The Canadian system of government is similar to the American system, with a central federal government and a system of provincial governments. The British North America Act of 1867 is like the United States Constitution in its creation of a federated system. The Act delegates certain authorities and responsibilities to the provincial government and reserves others for the federal government.

Under the federated system the regulation of the practice of nursing is delegated to the state or provincial legislatures. The practice of nursing is not subject to regulation by Congress or the Canadian Parliament. One exception will be discussed in detail. When Congress or the Canadian Parliament does enact legislation affecting the nursing profession it has nationwide effect.

It is important to note that the states and provinces have not redelegated the regulation of the nursing profession to any county or municipal body, so that at the present time the regulation of this and other professions is carried out at the state level.

Perhaps the most important result of state regulation of nursing, from the point of view of the nurse, is that each state has the authority to issue its own nursing licenses. A license issued in one state does not give the nurse the right to practice in another state. In addition, each state legislature has the authority to enact laws that affect the practice of nursing within that state; it does not have the authority to enact laws that affect the practice of nursing in another state. Neither may the state legislature violate the common law rights of the nurse guaranteed her by the federal and state constitutions. Any act of the state legislature in contradiction of the state or federal constitution is null and void in its operation.

In the chapter on nursing practice acts it will be seen that the right of each state to regulate nursing within the state has resulted in widely varying nursing laws—sometimes substantially so.

The Common Law System

The common law system, found in both the United States and Canada, has been inherited from the British common law system and is based upon the principle that it is humanly impossible for the legislature to enact in advance laws that will anticipate the legal aspects of all human acts. Instead of trying to pass laws or codes that will cover all situations, the legislature in a common law country attempts to be as specific as possible in its enactments and leave it to the courts to fill in the gaps. The courts do this by attempting to apply the general principles to the specific situations that arise. In this respect the courts serve in a legislative capacity, but they are not completely uncontrolled since they must abide by existing statutes and use them to guide their actions. The courts are also bound by the precedent system, whereby a lower court in a state must follow the decisions of higher state courts as if they were laws enacted by the legislature. There is a procedure that a court can use to overrule precedents, or refuse to abide by them, but these situations are unusual and will not be discussed here.

When a state court has made a decision, by legislating, by filling in the gaps, or by interpreting a statute, that decision becomes part of the common law of that state. It becomes as binding a law as if it were an enactment of the state legislature. If the state legislature does not react favorably to the court decision, it can enact a specific statute to cover the situation, and this specific law then takes precedence over the court decision.

The essence of the common law system, therefore, is that law by judicial precedence, or judge-made law, is as binding as law enacted by the legislative body. This can be contrasted to civil law in which elaborate codes enacted by the legislature seek to predict all human experiences and the legal aspects thereof.

France is a good example of a nation which exists under a civil law system. The Codes of Napoleon still prevail as a major part of French law. Because of the historic French influence, both the Province of Quebec and the State of Louisiana have combinations of common and civil law systems.

The distinction beween civil law and criminal law is sometimes confused with the distinction between common law and civil law. The simplest distinction between civil and criminal law is that civil law controls the legal actions of individuals and criminal law controls the legal actions between an individual and a state. However, this is an artificial distinction because civil law, for example corporate law, can also regulate actions between an individual and a state. Perhaps the simplest distinction one can make is to say that criminal law involves fines or imprisonment. We shall say that any law that provides for a fine or imprisonment for the individual is a criminal law, and all others are civil laws.

Malpractice has traditionally been a subject for action by common law. We rarely find any legislative enactment which states that a certain type of conduct is or is not malpractice. Except in those instances in which an individual is brought before the courts to be prosecuted for a criminal act, or in which there is a serious difference as to a question of fact, the questions before the court are limited to interpretations of statutes and the common law, sometimes to determine the constitutionality of the legislation or the court action.

In a malpractice lawsuit the key legal question is how the high courts of that state reacted to similar claims of malpractice. If the subject of the lawsuit is one of first instance within the state, the judges and lawyers representing the various parties are very apt to look to judicial decisions in other states or provinces as persuasive evidence of what the court should do in this case. Although a court is not bound to follow the precedents of other jurisdictions, it will usually do so. Courts usually accept the non-binding precedents of other jurisdictions and adopt them for their own when there are no precedents on a particular subject established by the courts of the states. Thus the judicial decisions of one state have great significance in other states.

The system of using precedents may suggest that the law is unclear and ill-defined, and that there is nothing but risk in an area in which one would expect to find security and protection. In reality, however, the whole common law system, including the system of precedents, is no less definite than the civil law system. Perhaps as many cases go to court to determine what the legislature really intended as are presented to the courts to determine the status of the common law.

The Nurse and the Law

Those provisions in the law which regulate the nurse's conduct in the event of an abortion and regulate the distribution of narcotics are criminal laws, because if the nurse participates in an illegal abortion or distributes narcotics for illegal purposes the legal penalty imposed upon her is a fine or imprisonment. However, criminal law is really a very small part of the body of law that is directly applicable to the practical or professional nurse.

The two major areas of the law of concern to the nurse, then, are (1) nursing practice acts and (2) malpractice. With a few exceptions these two subjects are matters of civil law, since there is no criminal penalty imposed in these areas. The major exception is that portion of the state nursing practice act that provides that it shall be unlawful for an individual to hold himself out as a licensed nurse when he is not so qualified and licensed.

The nursing practice act, which is an enactment of the state legislature, regulates the nurse's relation to the state in which she practices and is a matter of civil law. There is rarely any common law with respect to nurse licensure or any of the other subjects covered in the nursing practice act. The opposite is true with respect to the law of malpractice. With a few exceptions, the law of malpractice is common law, that is, judge-made law, and the system of precedents plays a key role in resolving malpractice cases, since it is impossible to legislate what constitutes malpractice in every situation. Only recently have the legislatures been exhibiting any interest in controlling what is malpractice or controlling the relative rights of the health practitioner and his patients with regard to malpractice.

The major exception has been the legislative enactment of the so-called statutes of limitations. These laws, which exist in all jurisdictions, provide that a lawsuit must be instituted within a specific period of time from the event under question. The failure to begin legal action within that time limit precludes the right to sue. This is an oversimplification of course, and the statutes of limitations will be discussed further in the chapter on malpractice. It suffices to point out at this time that this is one instance in which the legislature acts in the malpractice area. Even here it could be argued that the question is really one concerning legal procedures and not one involving the merits of malpractice claims.

In addition to precedents in nursing malpractice cases, there are precedents in other malpractice cases which may be followed in a legal action against a nurse. The system of using precedents enables an individual to determine what the law might be when there does not appear to be any firm law. When the lawyer advises his client, he is suggesting that the precedents lead him to predict that the courts will react in a given way because of the way they reacted in similar situations. The precedents are the basis for the lawyer's predictions.

In the law of malpractice as it pertains to the nurse it is necessary to make certain predictions. One can predict that the courts of states that do not have any common law on a subject will follow the decisions on that subject rendered by courts in other states. One can also predict that the courts will follow prior decisions rendered in that state and not overrule the precedents. And one can predict that the principles established by the courts in malpractice actions against one practitioner of the healing arts will be followed in a similar situation involving a practitioner of a different healing art. In the area of malpractice there are some situations which recur. The legal profession knows what a court will do in a specific kind of case because they know what the court has done in similar cases. When attorneys and their clients are able to predict what a court will do in a given instance there is no need to take a case to court. If the facts of the case and the precedents are clear, the parties are in a position to "settle out of court." This means that they arrive at their legal conclusion and provide for recompensation of the injured party without going to court.

The healing professions continue to present new kinds of malpractice cases, and there has been some change in court decisions in malpractice cases that lead many of these lawsuits back to the courtroom. The nurse can find some measure of protection against arbitrary legal actions being brought against her in the fact that an attorney will not accept from a patient a case that he cannot expect to win. Other questions of this nature, such as the nuisance value of a lawsuit, and so forth, will be discussed in the chapters on malpractice (chapters 4 and 5).

Summary

From this brief outline of the law we can make some general conclusions about the law as it pertains to the nurse:

As a nurse and as an individual the nurse has legal rights and responsibilities under federal and state law.

Certain acts of the nurse are subject to criminal law and criminal penalties.

Regulation of the practice of nursing is generally a matter of state legislation.

Malpractice is a subject of judge-made, common law.

Legal precedents also allow us to predict what the courts will do in a particular lawsuit.

Glossary

accident—An unforeseen event that occurs without design or intent on the part of the person whose act causes it. When the nurse's negligence contributes to the occurrence of the event it cannot be said to be an accident.

action—The legal and formal demand of one's rights from another person or party, made and insisted on in a court of law. A party suffering injury caused by the conduct of another is said to have a "cause of action" against the other.

admission against interest—An individual's voluntary acknowledgment of the existence of certain facts contrary to his interests. A nurse who says "It was my fault" after the patient suffers an injury is making an admission against interest.

appellant—The party who, dissatisfied with the disposition of a case at the trial level, appeals to a higher court. The one who appeals.

assault—See *technical assault.*

assault and battery—A criminal charge, as distinguished from *technical assault*, which is a civil matter. Criminal assault and battery can be separated into two parts. Assault is the threat to do battery. One person assaults another by threatening to do physical harm to the other. The physical harm constitutes the battery.

breach of contract—A failure, not necessarily willful, to comply with the terms of a valid contract. A failure by a party to a contract to perform those acts he is obligated to perform under the provisions of the contract.

civil law—A statutory law, as opposed to common or judge-made law. A nursing practice act is a civil law of a state. Civil law can also be contrasted to criminal law. Civil law affects relations between individuals while criminal law affects the relation between an individual and the government.

common law—Judge-made law. Professional responsibility is generally a matter of common law. Common law is not found in the statute books, but it is just as binding as civil law.

consent—Voluntarily yielding the will to the proposition of another. When a patient consents to a particular action he is prevented from later asserting that such action was taken without his consent. Consent is meaningful only when given by a competent person and when all the pertinent facts are presented to him. Touching another without consent, expressed or implied, is a *technical assault.*

contract—An agreement between two or more competent persons, upon sufficient consideration, to do or not to do some lawful act.

contributory negligence—An act or omission on the part of the patient, amounting to a want of ordinary care, concurring with the negligent act or omission of the practitioner as the proximate cause of the injury.

crime—An action in violation of the laws of a state, which can result in a fine, imprisonment, or capital punishment. Generally, misdemeanors are minor offenses, which are not included within the general usage of the term crime, although misdemeanors are technically crimes. The term crime has become limited by usage to mean the deeper offenses.

criminal law—Criminal law is that law pertaining to crimes, criminals, and punishment of persons who violate the law. Violation of a criminal law results in punishment by the state.

damages—A pecuniary compensation recovered in the courts by any person who has suffered loss, detriment, or injury, whether to his person, property or rights, through the wrongful act, omission, or negligence of another.

defendant—The party being sued. The action is against the defendant.

delict—An offense, wrong, or an injury. A violation of a duty owed to another or to the state.

duty of care—The legal duty of the nurse to her patients to possess and exercise such skills and care as exercised by the other prudent nurses in the community under the same or similar circumstances.

duty of care (specialist)—The same as above, except it must compare to that of the other prudent specialists in the community.

ex delicto—From a delict, tort, fault, crime or malfeasance. In contrast to *ex contractu* (out of a contract).

expert witness—A person who possesses special or peculiar training, or knowledge acquired from practical experience. A nurse qualified to testify in court as to what the ordinarily prudent nurse in the community would do under a given set of circumstances.

expressed consent—As opposed to implied consent. A patient requesting that a specific procedure be performed has given his expressed consent to that procedure. If the doctor or nurse explains and suggests a procedure and the patient orally agrees, the patient has given his expressed consent.

expressed contract—A contract in which the parties have declared orally or in writing the terms of their agreement.

false imprisonment—Wrongful restraint of an individual against his will. Preventing a patient from leaving the medical office or hospital may constitute false imprisonment.

fault—A negligent or improper act or omission that results in an injury to another.

grievance—A complaint or reason for complaint that an injury was caused by the fault or delict of another. The term is commonly used to indicate a situation in which a patient has a complaint against a doctor or nurse and seeks redress through the medical or nursing association rather than by filing a lawsuit.

good faith—Honesty of intent, and freedom from knowledge of circumstances that ought to put the holder upon inquiry. Generally an insufficient defense in a malpractice lawsuit.

Good Samaritan legislation—Statutes enacted in some states providing that practitioners of the healing arts (in some states limited to physicians) who render aid in an emergency situation are not liable to the injured party for alleged malpractice unless there is a showing of bad faith or willful wrong.

hearsay rule—Excludes evidence that proceeds not from the personal knowledge of the witness, but from the mere repetition of what he has heard others say. Such evidence is unusually excluded because of the lack of opportunity to cross-examine the person making the statement out of court.

implied consent—When expressed consent has not been given by the patient, consent may be implied at law by the actions of the parties.

implied contract—(See *contract.*) A contract created at law because of the relationship between parties. A patient and doctor who do not mention fees impliedly contract that the doctor will charge a reasonable fee for his services. This is a contract that the law makes for parties because they have not made one for themselves by entering into an expressed contract.

injury—The legal loss which the patient suffers and alleges to have been caused by the negligence of the nurse. May be physical, mental or monetary.

insurer—The company accepting premiums in return for specific or speculative benefits in the insurer. The insurance company issuing the policy is the insurer.

judgment—The official and authentic decision of a court upon the respective rights and claims of parties in litigation. Commonly, the amount awarded to a successful patient.

jurisprudence—The knowledge or source of the law. Nursing jurisprudence is the knowledge and source of the law as applied to nursing.

liability—Legal responsibility to account for one's wrongful actions by making financial restitution to the injured party.

licensure—This relates to the license issued by a state authorizing an individual to engage in a profession which is prohibited to all but those licensed by the state to engage in that profession.

litigation—The process of a lawsuit. When two parties are involved in a lawsuit they are said to be involved in litigation. The court litigates or determines the respective rights of the parties to litigation.

malfeasance—The doing of an act which the doer has no right to do or which he agreed not to do. Sometimes this term is erroneously used interchangeably with misfeasance, which is doing an act in an improper manner.

malpractice—One part of the law of negligence as applied to the professional person. Any professional misconduct, unreasonable lack of skill, or lack of fidelity in professional duties.

mitigation of damages—The minimization of damages. An injured patient has a duty to mitigate or minimize damages even though the injury was originally caused by the negligence of another.

negligence—The omission to do something that a reasonable nurse, guided by those considerations that ordinarily regulate a nurse's affairs, would do; or the act of doing something that a reasonable and ordinarily prudent nurse would not do.

nudum pactum—A bare contract, one not binding at law.

plaintiff—The person asserting a cause of action and instituting a lawsuit.

police power—The authority of the state to enact laws to protect the public, by means of a nursing practice act for example, reserved to the states by the Constitution.

principal and agent—A relationship in which one person performs services for another, whereby the performing person works under the direct control and supervision of another. Generally the nurse is the agent of the doctor. An agency exists when one person has the authority to direct and control the other and he need not exercise this authority for an agency to be established.

privileged communication—The information given to the doctor or nurse by the patient in order to secure medical treatment. Apparently some states will not let these communications be disclosed in court if the patient so requests.

proximate cause—A causal relationship must be established between the patient's injury and the nurse's negligence for the nurse to be liable; her negligence must have been the *proximate cause* of the injury.

question of fact—For example, the determination of whether the nurse exercised reasonable skill and care is a question of fact. The jury determines all questions of fact and considers all evidence going to the proof of facts. The judge considers the questions of law, e.g. whether or not, as a matter of law, certain evidence is legally admissable in court and whether the jury may consider such evidence.

question of law—See *question of fact.*

reasonable care—The degree of care that the reasonable nurse would exercise. The nurse's defense in a malpractice lawsuit is that she used reasonable care.

remittitur—The judge's decision that the plaintiff has been overcompensated for his injury and that he should remit part of the judgment. Generally a judge will give the plaintiff the option of making a *remittitur* or suffering a new trial.

res gestae—The circumstances, facts, and declarations that grow out of the main fact, are contemporaneous with it, and serve to illustrate its character. For example, the nurse saying "It was my fault" when an instrument slips and injures a patient.

res ipsa loquitur—The thing speaks for itself. A legal doctrine, applied against the nurse or doctor in certain circumstances, that creates the presumption of negligence. Applicable when the injury was caused by an instrument under the exclusive control of the doctor or nurse, which would not cause injury unless the doctor or nurse is negligent, for example, an X-ray machine falling on a patient who is sitting.

res judicata—A thing judicially acted upon or decided. The concept that a case finally determined will not be retried.

respondeat superior—The legal concept whereby the principal is legally liable for the negligent acts of the agent committed in the course of employment. Both parties become liable for the action of the agent.

stare decisis—To stand by decided cases; to uphold precedents; to maintain former adjudications. Under this rule a judge is generally obligated to follow decisions rendered by equal or higher courts of his state.

statute of frauds—The state law that sets forth the contracts that must be evidenced by writing to be enforceable.

statute of limitations—The state law that sets forth a time limit within which a legal action must be commenced before the right to bring the action is lost. Usually six years for contracts and two years for personal injuries.

technical assault—Touching another without his consent, expressed or implied. A nurse who administers an anesthetic without the consent of the patient would be guilty of a technical assault.

tort—A legal wrong committed upon the person or property of another independent of contract. A negligent act resulting in an injury is a tort.

2 *The Nursing Practice Act*

Under the police power reserved to each state by the United States Constitution, and under the authority vested in each province of Canada pursuant to the British North America Act, each state and province has the legislative authority to regulate the practice of nursing within its boundaries.

The typical nursing practice act provides:

A definition of professional nursing.

A definition of practical nursing.

The creation of a board of nursing examiners.

Responsibilities of the board of nursing examiners.

Requirements for a license to practice professional nursing.

Requirements for a license to practice practical nursing.

Exemptions from licensing requirements.

Prohibitions and penalties for engaging in the unlicensed practice of nursing.

Grounds for revocation of a nursing license.

Requirement that a nursing license be registered.

Fees for licensure and licensure examinations.

Temporary practice without a license.

Reciprocity for persons licensed in other states.

This chapter will discuss occupational licensing in general and nursing licensure in particular.

Occupational Licensing

In 1958 William L. Frederick, Ph.D., then eastern representative for the Council of State Governments, presented a paper entitled "The History and Philosophy of Occupational Licensing Legislation in the United

States" at a symposium conducted by the American Dental Association. Some quotations from Dr. Frederick's paper follow. It should be noted that he is referring to all occupational licensing and not just nursing licensure.

> Of course, licensing serves more than these professional interests; it also protects the interests of the general public. This is the legal basis for licensing, for such legislation may be justified only if it protects the health, safety, or welfare of the people.
>
> I think it is clear that licensing assists a group in achieving a professional or occupational identity. It helps to define the boundaries of a profession or skill and says that the application of knowledge within these boundaries is a part of a specific profession. I believe also that licensing may help individuals to achieve greater financial compensation for their work, though this result may be more easily demonstrated in some of the fields subject to licensing than in others. But these goals, though they are important to individuals and small groups, are secondary to the basic purpose of licensing. The important question is: How effectively does licensing protect the public interest, the public health, safety and welfare?
>
> Licensing legislation of this type does not serve the public interest so much as it protects the interests of those already practicing within the state. The increasing mobility of our population makes these barriers more and more serious and more and more detrimental to the best interests of the public.

Dr. Frederick describes three yardsticks to be used in evaluating licensure proposals. First, it must be clearly shown that there is a need to protect the public health, safety, or welfare. Second, the occupation must be clearly delineated as a separate and distinct area of work. He adds,

> Here the relationships among professions are important and should be considered when it is proposed to extend licensing to a new field.

Dr. Frederick refers to the third yardstick as follows:

> Third, a legislator may inquire about the organized association in the field, its relationship to the profession or occupation as a whole and its ability to assume some of the obligations of the licensing process. . . . The attitudes and abilities of the association may determine whether licensing will serve the public interest.

Professor Malcum B. Parsons, in his book *The Use of the Licensing Power by the City of Chicago* (University of Illinois Press, Urbana, 1952), makes some general remarks about licensing that are especially significant for the licensing of professional and practical nurses.

> Where licensing enters into the service of public health, safety and morals, its supposed intent is to eliminate from activities con-

trolled by recognized public need those who will not, or cannot conform to desirable standards. The problem, however, lies in the public divorcement of standards from public need. Where this occurs, either through the overwhelming reach of private interest in both the determination and operation of public policy or through the influence of subsequently changed circumstances, licensing becomes less an instrument of some public purpose than an official sanctioning of the narrower desires of the private groups it ostensibly controls.

The licensing of professional and practical nurses seems to qualify under the guidelines suggested by Dr. Frederick and to fall outside the dangers warned of by Professor Parsons. Nursing meets Dr. Frederick's first test because it is undeniably in the public interest to license nurses. The license protects the public by safeguarding that the nurse has met minimum standards of education and training. Since nursing can be clearly defined as a separate and distinct profession, the second test for licensing is also met.

Nursing Licensure

The first nursing practice acts were adopted around 1910 in New York, New Jersey, and North Carolina. At the present time there are nursing practice acts in all states and provinces. The essential element of nursing licensure is that provision in the law of each state or province which specifies that no person shall practice as a professional or practical nurse without a license. And the law proceeds to provide the penalties for practicing without a license. This is similar to the laws that define medicine and dentistry and specify that it is a criminal act to engage in medical or dental practice without a state license.

Since each state and province issues its own professional licenses, the possession of one state license does not by itself permit the holder to practice her profession in another state. However, the possession of one state's license may be the basis on which another state will issue a license.

Definition of Professional Nursing

Because each state and provincial legislature enacts its own nursing practice act, we find there are almost as many definitions of professional nursing as there are legislatures. The American Nurses' Association recommends the following definition, which has been adopted by some legislatures:[1]

ANA :

> The practice of professional nursing means the performance for compensation of any act in the observation, care and counsel of the ill, injured or infirm, or in the maintenance of health or prevention of illness of others, or in the supervision and teaching of other personnel, or in the administration of medications and treatments as prescribed by a licensed physician or dentist; requiring substantial specialized judgment and skill and based on knowledge and application of the principles of biological, physical and social science. The foregoing shall not be deemed to include acts of diagnosis or prescription of therapeutic or corrective measures.

The definition of professional nursing practice is important for two reasons. First, it delineates the area of professional nursing, to make it clear when a license is required for providing these professional services. Second, the definition protects the nurse from the charge of unlicensed practice of medicine.

It is remarkable that there have been relatively few lawsuits brought against unlicensed persons for the crime of engaging in nursing practice without a license. For the unlicensed person the problem is that his actions will fall within the definition of the practice of professional nursing and will constitute a criminal violation of law. In the professions of medicine and dentistry there are constant battles to prosecute those individuals who engage in professional practices without the benefit of education or licensure. Perhaps the relatively good experience in nursing stems from the fact that physicians, dentists, and hospitals are careful in selecting their employees. The public, too, has become educated to the need to employ only a licensed person for nursing functions.

For the licensed nurse the problem is to avoid conduct that passes from the realm of nursing into the realm of medicine or dentistry and makes her guilty of practicing those professions without a license. The medical practice act defines medical practice and usually states that a nurse who is practicing her profession under the supervision and control of a physician is exempt from the medical practice act insofar as she acts under the doctor's supervision and control. There is a traditional attitude on the part of the physician and surgeon, however, that the professional nurse is permitted by law to perform any medical function that he wishes to delegate to her. Naturally there are restrictions on delegable functions. For example, the nurse may not perform surgery or make a diagnosis. The functions that nurses are permitted to perform by delegation are generally in the area of mechanical acts that do not require the exercise of any medical discretion, and there have been few legal complaints about functions delegated to the nurse by the physician and there have been very few cases brought against nurses for the alleged unlicensed practice of medicine.

In general the nursing practice acts do not help resolve the problems of unlicensed medical practice because they are too vague or ambiguous. The newer nursing practice acts for the most part describe in greater detail the functions that can be performed by a nurse and, like the ANA definition, attempt to distinguish those functions that can be performed independently of the physician from those requiring that the nurse act under the direction and control of a physician.

There is an obvious conflict in the idea of defining nursing with substantial arguments on each side. It could be argued that the statute should provide that the nurse is permitted to perform any service delegated by the physician rather than stating specific services, because the legislature may unintentionally omit some important services. The opposing argument is that if the nurse can perform any delegated function the nurse is in reality practicing medicine.

The professional nurse should be familiar with the definition of professional nursing within her own state to make sure that she is not acting in an improper and illegal manner. If the nurse thinks that the law in her state does not permit her to perform a specific function that has been assigned to her, she should discuss this with a member of the State Board of Nursing Examiners. Community custom often helps resolve ambiguities in the law. Some functions may not appear to the nurse to fall within the definition of professional nursing, but she may be safe in performing them because they are commonly accepted in her state as a part of professional nursing practice.

In 1961 a California court[2] nicely summed up the law with respect to legal functions of the nurse: "It has generally been recognized that the functions of nurses and physicians overlap to some extent, and a licensed nurse when acting under the direction and supervision of a licensed physician, is permitted to perform certain tasks which, without such direction and supervision, would constitute the illegal practice of medicine or surgery."

We now mention some of the more common elements of nursing practice acts to illustrate the difficulties that may be encountered in interpreting these acts and how they might be avoided.

COMPENSATION. A nursing practice act should limit the definition of nursing practice to nursing services provided "for compensation." This is consistent with the observation made by a Wisconsin court[3] in 1931 that the law does not prohibit anyone from acting as a nurse, but prohibits anyone from practicing as a registered, trained, certified, or graduate nurse without a certificate of registration. Most states also permit relatives, friends, and servants to act as nurses when they are not receiving compensation, or when the compensation they receive is incidental to the services they perform.

INDEPENDENT AND DEPENDENT FUNCTIONS. A good nursing practice act will separate the independent functions (what nurse can do on her own) from the dependent functions (what she can do only, under the direction of a doctor).

PHYSICIAN AND DENTIST. Most of the definitions of nursing practice that include the statement that the nurse must work under the direct supervision of a physician specifically state "physician and dentist," as does the ANA definition. If the dentist is not specifically mentioned, however, there is some serious question as to whether or not the nurse can perform certain functions under the direct supervision of a dentist. It is likely that the court called upon to make this decision would find that the term physician here includes dentists, or it might find that it is assumed that the intent of the law was to permit the nurse to work under the direct supervision of a dentist. If the law does not provide for a nurse working for a dentist, the nurse risks a finding that she has been guilty of the unlicensed practice of dentistry when a dentist delegates certain functions to her. It is surprising that there has been no significant amount of legal action in this area. It is equally surprising that more dentists do not use chairside nurses in their dental practice, since the reading of the nursing and dental acts together would apparently permit the nurse to provide much important chairside assistance that cannot be legally provided by the dental assistant.

PROHIBITED ACTS. The definition of nursing practice should leave no doubt that certain acts are prohibited to the nurse. Among these are making a diagnosis, writing of prescriptions, and recommending therapeutic or corrective measures. These functions, even when performed under the supervision of a physician, would clearly appear to constitute the practice of medicine and should be clearly prohibited in the nursing practice law.

ADMINISTRATION OF MEDICAMENTS AND ANESTHETICS. A nurse may not inject medication into a patient except by order of a doctor, and she must use reasonable means to make sure that she has the drug called for by the doctor.[4] Neither may she prescribe medications. In 1967 a California court[5] considered a pharmacist's responsibility to fill a prescription signed by a nurse, and held that prescriptions authorized by a nurse are not valid.

In a few states the nursing practice law specifically states that the professional nurse may administer general anesthetics under the supervision and control of a physician. Among these states are Arizona, Kentucky, Washington and Ohio.

In California[6] the same result was achieved in 1936 by court decision.

In this lawsuit an injunction was sought by a group of physicians and surgeons to restrain the defendant nurse from administering general anesthetics in connection with operations. The doctors said that the nurse was engaged in the illegal practice of medicine. The court, however, held that the nurse was not engaged in the illegal practice of medicine since she was not "diagnosing" or "prescribing" while assisting in surgery, and her activities were under the control of surgeons.

The court stated that a licensed registered nurse could lawfully administer general anesthetics in connection with operations, under the immediate direction and supervision of a physician.

In 1961 this decision was reaffirmed by another California court[7] that stated, "It is common practice around the country for licensed physicians to authorize and permit persons not licensed as physicians to administer anesthetics."

If the general approach is that the nurse merely serves the function of providing trained hands to carry out the doctor's instructions, there would seem to be no reason to prohibit the nurse from acting as an anesthetist under the supervision and control of a physician. One writer in this field[8] states that it is generally accepted that the nurse can give anesthesia if she administers the anesthetic under the direction and supervision of the physician in charge. However the nurse may not lawfully perform the preliminary examination before giving the anesthetic.

Since the administration of anesthetics is an area of great physical danger to the patient and an area of legal danger to the nurse, the nurse should be particularly conversant with the nursing law of her own state with respect to administration of local or general anesthetics, and when she does have the authority to administer anesthetics or medications, she should do so only under the supervision of a doctor.

Definition of Practical Nursing

Most states have now legislatively designated a second level of nursing practice, practical nursing. The American Nurses' Association suggests the following definition of practical nursing:

ANA. The practice of practical nursing means the performance for compensation of selected acts in the care of the ill, injured, or infirm under the direction of a registered professional nurse or a licensed physician or a licensed dentist; and not requiring the substantial specialized skill, judgment and knowledge required in professional nursing.

If the definition of professional nursing is vague, the definition of practical nursing is even more so. Yet the definition suggested by the ANA is obviously more realistic and more meaningful than the definitions appearing in some of the state laws. For example:

> Practical nursing means the performance under the direction of a licensed physician, dentist or registered professional nurse of such simple nursing procedures as may be required in the care of a patient and the conservation of health.
>
> A practical nurse is a person who performs such nursing service as prescribed by a licensed physician, requiring a knowledge of simple nursing procedures but not requiring the professional knowledge and skills required for professional nursing.
>
> Practical nursing means the performance of nursing services for patients if while performing these services the nurse is at all times under the direction and supervision of a licensed physician or registered nurse acting under the supervision of a licensed physician.

The ANA definition of practical nursing is more precise than these definitions in that it mentions compensation. This is desirable, but since there have been few legal actions taken against individuals for the unlicensed practice of practical nursing, this is really not too important.

One immediate consequence of these definitions is that the professional nurse may be called upon to supervise the activities of the practical nurse. The professional nurse has a legal responsibility not to delegate functions to a practical nurse which are beyond her legal capacity and training. This will be discussed further in the chapter on malpractice.

Just as the professional nurse must avoid transgressing into medical practice, the practical nurse must be careful not to perform functions that constitute professional nursing practice, or even medical practice. Physicians who allow practical nurses to practice professional nursing are assisting in the violation of law and can lose their medical licenses for this offense. However there have been few prosecutions of physicians for this violation. One of the few lawsuits concerning a practical nurse who practiced medicine involved a practical nurse in New York who held herself as qualified in medicine by offering to vaccinate people against smallpox. She was not acting under the direction of a physician or carrying out his orders. She was found to be guilty of practicing medicine without a license.[9] An interesting aside was that the "serum" used by the nurse was water.

Although the definitions of practical nursing seem vague, the role of the practical nurse is easy to interpret in practice. Important assistance in determining the responsibilities of the practical nurse is available in the Statement of Functions of the Licensed Practical Nurse, approved by the American Nurses' Association and the National Federation of Licensed Practical Nurses.

Creation of a Board of Nursing Examiners

State or provincial law provides for the creation of a Board of Nursing Examiners. In most instances the Board is comprised of practicing nurses who are licensed within the state. The members of the board are usually appointed by the governor of the state. In many instances the governor selects members from a list of names submitted by the state nursing association, however many state laws have been changed to remove the statutory requirement that the governor appoint from a list submitted by the state professional association. The governor is always free to ask the state organization to recommend a candidate or candidates for vacancies on the state examining boards.

The qualifications for membership on the state nursing board are usually not less than those for licensure in the state. In some instances the law may require that the members of the board be graduated from a recognized college, even though college graduation is not a prerequisite for licensure in that state. Some nursing laws require that the examiner have had experience as a teacher or an administrator in a nursing education program and a specified number of years of actively engaging in nursing practice.

In some states the Board of Nursing Examiners includes lay persons in addition to professional nurses. This is not done in most professional licensing boards, however, and the practice is opposed by the American Nurses' Association. In some states statute requires that a committee of practical nurses assist the nursing board.

The nursing law usually specifies the number of years an individual may serve on the board and the means for removal of an unsatisfactory examiner. Most board members, and this includes other professions as well as nursing, receive little more for their time and effort on the state board than reimbursement for their expenses. Some state boards pay a modest per diem allowance to reimburse the examiner for the time and income she has lost while serving as an examiner.

Responsibilities of the Board of Nursing Examiners

The Nursing Board does not set the qualifications for licensure, since these are usually specified in the Nursing Practice Act. However the Board has the responsibility for reviewing applications to determine these qualifications, and to construct and administer the nursing examination. In most instances the Board of Nursing Examiners has this responsibility with respect to both professional and practical nursing, even though the membership of the board does not include practical nurses.

The administration of most professional licensing laws is customarily assigned to the state examining board. The nursing board maintains the registry of nurses and has important responsibilities for enforcing the law against the individual who has practiced this profession without licensure. Another important law enforcement function concerns the revocation or suspension of licenses of nurses who have violated the law, and most nursing practice acts specify the grounds for revocation or suspension of a nursing license. The board has the responsibility for instituting the legal action necessary to revoke or suspend the license.

Requirements for a License to Practice Professional Nursing

It is in the requirements for a license to practice professional nursing that we find the most significant differences among the states and provinces.

EDUCATION.   All states and provinces require that the nurse complete an approved course in nursing, either in a hospital or in an accredited teaching institution. Some states also specify that a nurse must have been graduated from high school as well. The latter requirement is not too relevant, since graduation from an approved nurses training program should be sufficient evidence of a secondary school education.

AGE.   Some nursing acts in Canada and the United States specify a minimum age for licensure. The most common age specified is 20, but some nursing acts require that the applicant be 21. This requirement does not seem to be justified, since the fact that the nurse has been graduated from an approved nursing education program should be sufficient proof of her maturity.

CITIZENSHIP.   Some nursing acts require that the applicant be a citizen or have declared her intention to become a citizen. This does not appear to be meaningful, since citizenship or intention to become a citizen would not seem to have any relevance to the individual's competence to assume the responsibilities of a licensed nurse.

GOOD MORAL CHARACTER.   All nursing laws require that the applicant for licensure demonstrate "good moral character." This requirement is obviously ambiguous, but it is useful in that it gives the board of nursing examiners a firm basis for denial of a nursing license to a person of "bad moral character." This power can be abused but does not seem to have presented any significant amount of controversy.

EXAMINATION.   Most nursing practice laws require that the individual pass an examination for licensure. According to the laws of some states the examination may be waived when the applicant has a valid nursing license issued by another state. There has been a trend in professional licensing toward giving graduates of accredited schools (or perhaps only the top graduates) licenses without examinations. The rationale is that the individual proved his competence at the time he graduated and there is no need for further proof. It is likely that in the future there will be less emphasis on state licensing examinations.

MEMBERSHIP IN A NURSING ASSOCIATION. Many of the Canadian provinces require that the nurse join the nursing association as a condition of licensure. This may be a very desirable requirement since it means that the nurse remains in contact with her professional organization. The requirement that an individual join an association as a condition of licensure is being introduced in the United States by other professional boards. There are at least two states which require that an attorney join the bar association as a condition of licensure. In the future we may find a more substantial number of states requiring membership in a professional organization.

Requirements for a License to Practice Practical Nursing

As one might expect, the requirements for a practical nursing license are less stringent than the requirements for a professional nursing license. This is directly related to the relevant responsibilities of the professional and practical nurse.

EDUCATION. The most important requirement for establishing eligibility for the examination or otherwise qualifying for practical nursing licensure is the completion of a state accredited educational program in practical nursing. Naturally the length of this program is shorter than the educational program for the professional nurse.

AGE. The minimum age for licensure as a practical nurse, when specified by statute, is usually less than that required for the professional nurse. The most common age specified is 18.

EXAMINATION. Most states require that an individual pass an examination for licensure. However there are two alternatives to examination as a means for securing a practical nursing license. Licensure in another state may make the nurse eligible for licensure without examination by virtue of a reciprocity agreement or "endorsement," whereby licensure in one jurisdiction will be accepted as proof of qualification for licensure in another jurisdiction. The second alternative to licensure pertains only to those nurses who have been working as practical nurses prior to the enactment of the state law that requires licensure. This provision, the so-called "grandfather's statute," permits persons to continue to practice if they have done so for a substantial period prior to the time that law was enacted.

Grandfather Clause

Exemptions from Licensing Requirements

The nursing acts provides that it shall be unlawful for an individual to practice nursing without a license, but the acts also states that certain classes of persons shall be exempt from the licensing requirement. One obvious exemption is the physician or dentist who is permitted to practice his profession without benefit of an nursing license.

EMPLOYEE OF A FEDERAL AGENCY.   One exemption commonly found in nursing acts provides that an employee of the federal government who practices her profession as a part of her official duties need not have a state license. Most state licensing laws make this exemption for federal employees who limit themselves to their official duties while in that state. This exemption is somewhat gratuitous, since it is doubtful that the state could require the federal employee to hold a state license. Since the states have not attempted to enforce their licensing laws against federal employees, the question is academic.

THE EMERGENCY.   The unlicensed person who renders medical assistance in an emergency situation is not guilty of unlicensed practice of nursing according to the laws of most states. This charge, or the charge of unlicensed practice of medicine, is rarely levied in a true emergency situation. The nurse who engages in medical practice in the emergency situation is likewise protected against a charge of unlicensed practice of medicine if a true emergency existed and there was no physician readily available.

This exemption is not always specified in the nursing practice act, but most courts will accept the theory that there is an exception created by the benefit to the public in having unlicensed persons render first aid in emergency situations.

STUDENT NURSES.   Student nurses practice nursing but are also exempt from nursing licensure laws, necessarily so. Otherwise they could not even learn nursing. A student has to be careful, however, not to give the impression that she is a licensed nurse, or she may find that she is treated as a licensed nurse for the purpose of malpractice charges.

SPIRITUAL NURSING.   Most state nursing laws provide an exemption for the person who nurses by prayer or other spiritual means. This is another gratuitous exemption, since it is doubtful that spiritual nursing actually falls within the definition of nursing.

AWAITING LICENSURE.   Many nursing laws take legislative cognizance of the fact that a few weeks or months may elapse from the time that the nurse completes her training until she can take the examination for licensure. For this reason many states permit the nurse to practice without a license for a stated period, usually six months, after her completion of a qualified course in nursing, while waiting the next licensure examination. However, this exemption only applies when the nurse has met the other qualifications for license, and it does not exist in all states.

A similar exemption is found in state laws that provide that a nurse licensed in another state who is otherwise qualified may practice for a specific period without a license, pending the acceptance of her application for licensure under reciprocity laws. The legislatures obviously feel that it is in the public interest to permit the nurse to practice while awaiting formal action by the board of nursing examiners.

PERSONS WHO DO NOT CALL THEMSELVES NURSES. A license is required only when an individual practices nursing for compensation and presents herself to the public as a nurse. Persons who perform nursing duties but do not indicate that they are professional or practical nurses are generally exempt from the licensing requirements. There are no legal prohibitions against a friend or a member of a family providing nursing services even though she is not licensed.

Some nursing practice acts retain a specific prohibition against using the title "R.N." or "Licensed Practical Nurse" as the sole means of controlling unlicensed practice. In these states anyone can act as a nurse providing that she does not use these titles. Happily, most states are amending their laws in order to make them stricter.

NURSES, AIDES, AND OTHERS. A professional nurse is legally entitled to engage in practical nursing if she so chooses, and is exempt from the practical nursing requirements in this case. In addition, nurse's aides, orderlies, and others who carry out the directions of the nurse are exempt from the nursing license requirements if they act only under the direction of a nurse or other licensed person, and do not engage in acts which are specifically allocated only to licensed persons by the nursing statutes.

Grounds for Revocation of a Nursing License

In addition to its authority to grant nursing licenses, the Board of Nursing Examiners usually has the authority to revoke or suspend nursing licenses. When the Board of Nursing Examiners believes that there are grounds for the revocation or suspension of a nursing license, a hearing is held to determine if punitive action should be taken. The hearing is usually conducted as a quasi-judicial proceeding that permits the nurse to be faced with the charges and to respond in her own defense. The usual statutory provisions pertaining to a hearing for revoking or suspending a nursing license specify the nurse's rights with respect to the time and place of the hearing, and the procedural safeguards that protect her against any arbitrary or capricious act on the part of the Board. In most instances the nurse is entitled to be represented by legal counsel at this hearing, and it is strongly recommended that a nurse who is called before the Board for such a hearing retain an attorney to represent her throughout the proceedings.

Persons aggrieved by the decision of the nursing board in revoking or suspending their license are free to appeal to a court of competent jurisdiction from the actions of the board. In some states the nursing law provides for an appeal to another state agency from the board's decision and specifies that this step must be taken prior to any appeal to the courts.

The courts are very quick to overrule the action of any professional board that results in the revocation of a professional license. For violations of the nursing law, the court prefers penalties that are less severe than revocation of the license to practice, which they agree should be imposed only in extreme cases.

The nursing practice act of each state and province specifies the acts that subject the nurse to discipline. Sometimes the practice acts contain some vague grounds for discipline, such as conduct unbecoming to a nurse, that seem to be catch-alls for all kinds of misconduct. The courts tend to shy away from permitting a board to revoke or suspend a professional license on such vague grounds.

In addition to the particular cases to be discussed, the nursing act may include any other offenses which the legislature believes to be sufficient grounds for disciplinary action. The only restriction upon the legislature is that it must be clearly shown that these grounds are based upon the public interest in maintaining a high level of public health. There must be no arbitrariness or capriciousness in the legislative listing of the grounds for discipline.

FRAUD IN LICENSING. The most common ground for discipline found in the nursing and other professional laws is fraud or deception in obtaining the license. The individual who has obtained a nursing license by this means is not safe in assuming that the deception, once practiced, will be sufficient to enable her to retain the license. Falsifying school records, age, past criminal history, etc., are all sufficient grounds for revocation or suspension of the nursing license.

CRIMINAL OR IMMORAL ACTS. Some nursing laws state that the nurse is subject to discipline if she commits any "criminal or immoral act." Others state that she is subject to discipline if she is found guilty of a criminal or immoral act by a competent court. In the first instance the nursing board must decide whether or not the nurse is guilty of a criminal or immoral act, and in the second it merely relies on a court finding. It is obviously preferable to leave these findings to the courts rather than to have the nursing board make these determinations.

NEGLIGENCE AND MALPRACTICE. Many nursing practice acts provide that the nursing license can be revoked or suspended if the licensee is guilty of gross or continued negligence and malpractice. However, it is often difficult for the board to make factual determinations that will justify discipline. The usual malpractice lawsuit involves only the patient and the nurse (and doctor) and not the nursing board, so the question of licensure is not usually involved. When it is, there must be a finding of continued or gross malpractice to justify board action.

DRUGS AND ALCOHOL. Many nursing licensing laws provide for discipline in the event that the licensee becomes addicted to drugs or alcohol. In this case "addicted" undoubtedly means usage to such an extent as to interfere with performance of professional functions or otherwise make it dangerous to permit the nurse to continue to serve in her professional capacity. This is perhaps the most common ground for revocation of a professional license.

ABORTION. Some nursing laws specifically state that participating in the performance of an illegal abortion constitutes grounds for discipline. Under these laws it would appear that the nurse can lose her license for performing an illegal abortion, or for assisting a doctor in what she knows to be an illegal abortion.

Fees and Registration

In many instances the nursing board operates solely from the fees it collects. The nursing laws usually specify the fee which must accompany an application for a license to practice professional or practical nursing. This fee is usually not returned if the individual is found to be ineligible for licensure. Some nursing laws set maximum and minimum allowable fees, and the determination of the actual fee is made by the Board of Nursing Examiners. Another fee may be required when the nurse is licensed, and is also set in the nursing law.

The nurse may register with the clerk of the county court or with the Board of Nursing Examiners. The laws of most states and provinces now require annual or biennial license reregistration, and failure to reregister may result in immediate suspension of the nursing license. In any event the nurse should be familiar with the reregistration requirements of the jurisdiction in which she is registered.

Summary

The nurse should be familiar with the nursing practice act of the jurisdiction in which she intends to practice. She cannot rely on the nursing act of one jurisdiction to provide her with the information needed for practice in another jurisdiction. The nurse or student who intends to go to a state or province other than the one in which she was trained should write to that jurisdiction's board of nursing examiners asking for copies of the nursing practice law and the requirements for licensure. The pertinent addresses can undoubtedly be found in any nursing school library; however, if the nurse or student cannot obtain the exact address, she may write to the "Board of Nursing Examiners, State of _____, State Capitol, State of _____," which in most instances will be a sufficient address.

References

1. In 1961 the American Nurse's Association prepared a two page memorandum that presents the association's position in "Legal Definition of Nursing."
2. Magit v. Board of Medical Examiners, 366 P. 2d 816 (Calif. 1961).
3. Nickley v. Eisenberg, 206 Wisc. 265 (1931).
4. C. L. Cusumano, Malpractice law dissected for quick grasping. New York, Medicine-Law Press, Inc., 1962, p. 118.
5. Randle v. California State Board of Pharmacy, 49 Cal. Rpt. 489 (1967).
6. Chalmers-Francis v. Nelson, 57 P. 2d 1312 (Calif. 1936).
7. Magit v. Board of Medical Examiners, *supra.*
8. Cusumano, page 117.
9. People v. Steinberg, 73 N.Y.S. 2d 475.

3 Ethics, Licensure, Malpractice, and Grievance

Ethics, licensure, malpractice, and grievance may present some confusion to the nurse. Each is distinct and worth separate consideration.

Ethics

Ethics involves the relationship between the nurse and the nursing association. When a nurse joins a professional society she agrees to abide by its principles of ethics. Although there is no requirement that a nurse belong to the American Nurses' Association in order to practice, about one-fourth of the American nurses belong to this society.

When a nurse violates the principles of ethics of a nursing association, the most severe discipline that it can impose is expulsion from membership. The society does not have the authority to revoke the nurse's license to practice nursing, or to determine whether or not she has been guilty of malpractice. The nurse should be familiar with the codes of ethics of her local and state associations as well as with the principles of ethics of the American Nurses' Association, since all three codes are binding upon the member. In its code of ethics (reprinted as an appendix at the end of this book), the American Nurses' Association sets out broad general principles, which may be supplemented by the state and local codes of ethics.

Licensure

The responsibility for issuing licenses to practice nursing rests with the state boards of nursing examiners. If the nurse violates the nursing practice act, it is the duty and the responsibility of the state board of examiners to institute the proceedings for the suspension or the revocation of her license. Although licensure within the state is a prerequisite for membership in the nursing association, the association cannot issue or revoke a license.

The nursing practice act of each state specifies the grounds for revoking or suspending a license to practice nursing. If the nurse's license is revoked her membership in the nursing association is automatically terminated. The violation of the principles of ethics is not itself grounds for revoking the license, although a situation could arise in which the same course of conduct could be construed to constitute a violation of the principles of ethics and a violation of the nursing practice act.

The code of ethics imposes a higher standard on the nurse than the nursing practice act. When the nurse is licensed she agrees to abide by the standards of the practice act; when she enters the society, she agrees to abide by higher standards, the society's principles of ethics. Therefore the nurse can be unethical as far as the nursing association is concerned and still retain her license to practice.

Malpractice

While the code of ethics represents the nurse's relationship with the profession's society and licensure represents the nurse's relationship with the state in which she practices, malpractice and grievances concern the nurse's relationship with her patients. If a patient believes that the nurse has been guilty of some unfair practice, his recourse is the institution of a lawsuit for malpractice, for breach of contract, or for some violation of his legal rights.

Some of the grounds for which the patient might sue the nurse may also be grounds for revocation of her license or membership in the nursing association; however the patient who is aggrieved cannot expel the member or revoke the license. The most that the patient can do is bring the controversy to the attention of the nursing association or the state board of nursing examiners, who are empowered to institute the appropriate proceedings against the nurse if such procedure is warranted.

If the board or the nursing association wishes to take such action, they must establish that the nurse has violated the principles of ethics and the nursing practice act, in addition to being guilty of malpractice. If the patient alleges that the nurse was negligent, this does not mean that the nurse violated the nursing practice act or that she was unethical. A nurse may have been negligent in that she used bad judgment in treating a patient, without having been unethical or in violation of the nursing practice act.

When a nurse loses a malpractice case or when the nurse's insurance company makes an out of court settlement with the patient, this by itself has no effect on the nurse's membership in the society or her license to practice. Malpractice is not grounds for expulsion from membership or for revocation of a license, for ethical nurses can lose malpractice cases. However, repeated malpractice claims may influence the board of nursing examiners to revoke the nurse's license on the grounds that she is totally incompetent or on similar grounds, as provided in the state nursing practice act.

Grievance

As a matter of law, the patient must take his own legal action against the nurse if he believes that he has been wronged. He may also bring this wrong to the attention of the nursing association or the nursing board, but his recourse is directly against the nurse.

State and local societies can set up a voluntary grievance program with its own grievance committee, before which patients can appear with their complaints. The committee can require the nurse, if she is a member of the society, to appear before them to tell her side of the story, and then they can make recommendations to the nurse and the patient. However the grievance committee has no authority to force the nurse and the patient to accept its decision. It merely invites the nurse and the patient, before the case is heard in court, to agree voluntarily to abide by its decision. If the nurse and the patient agree to do this, the grievance committee has served a useful function. If either party later refuses to abide by the decision, there is little likelihood that the committee can do anything about it. At most the committee can expel the nurse who refuses to abide by their decision after giving her assent.

The society grievance committee is frequently limited to hearing cases in which the patient asks for a fee refund. Grievance committees will not usually hear cases alleging that a nurse has overcharged a patient, because it is not the society's function to interfere with the nurse's determination of fees. Also, the committee will not usually hear malpractice cases brought against a nurse who is being asked for damages, because they have no authority to force the nurse or her insurance company to pay damages even if they find that she was at fault.

In the case of a malpractice charge, a nurse should be cautious about submitting to a grievance committee until she has consulted with the insurance company that has issued her malpractice coverage. The company may feel that such participation would jeopardize their defense of the nurse if the patient ultimately sued for malpractice. Perhaps the most workable grievance committee procedures are those involving a group malpractice insurance policy in which the insurance company works with the society to set up a procedure that will discourage malpractice lawsuits.

4   *Malpractice*

Negligence and Malpractice

Negligence can be defined as:

> The omission to do something which a reasonable man, guided by those ordinary considerations which ordinarily regulate human affairs, would do, or the doing of something which a reasonable and prudent man would not do.

The law of negligence applies to everyone in his daily life. Whenever we do something that a reasonably prudent man would not do, or when we fail to do something that a reasonably prudent man would do, we are negligent.

Malpractice can be defined as:

> Any professional misconduct, unreasonable lack of skill or fidelity in professional or fiduciary duties, evil practice, or illegal or immoral conduct.

More specifically, malpractice means bad, wrong, or injudicious treatment of a patient professionally, in respect to a particular disease or injury; it results in injury, unnecessary suffering, or death to the patient; and it proceeds from ignorance, carelessness, want of proper professional skill, disregard of established rules or principles, negligence, or malicious or criminal intent. Malpractice, then, is one kind of negligence, and the definition of malpractice merely clarifies the term negligence in its application to the professional person.

There are two aspects of these definitions that should be understood. First, there is no mention of "good faith" in either definition. It is a well accepted principle of law that good faith is not a material factor in considering whether or not a particular act is negligent or constitutes malpractice. For example, the nurse may drive her car in an unreasonable manner and injure a pedestrian without intent to cause the injury. The nurse is negligent, even though she had good faith. The same is true in malpractice. The nurse may erroneously administer the wrong medication.

She acted in good faith but in an unreasonable manner by not reading the label. She is guilty of malpractice even though she acted in good faith. Second, the definitions of negligence and malpractice include omissions as well as commissions. A person is negligent who fails to act when the reasonably prudent man would act.

The significance of the distinction between malpractice and negligence is in the method of proving whether or not the nurse is liable to the patient. Because the distinction is generally based upon the actions of a professional as compared to the actions of a layman, the key question is whether or not the nurse was performing a professional function at the time of the injury. If she was performing an act that was professional in nature, it is a question of malpractice. If she was performing an act that was administrative or ministerial in nature, it is a question of negligence.

Generally the courts are willing to concede that the nurse is a professional person and is thus subject to the particular kind of negligence known as malpractice. The exceptions appear to be in regard to the statute of limitations which says that malpractice lawsuits must be commenced within a stated period after the injury occurs. In a number of cases the courts have stated that the nurse is not a professional within the meaning of the statute, so that the statute does not apply.

Duty of Care

Interpretations of the terms negligence and malpractice may be more meaningful if they are explained in terms of *duty of care*. In everyday life each individual has a duty of care towards others. A driver of a car has a duty of care toward others not to drive in such an unreasonable manner as to subject them to injuries. The nurse's duty of care is the standard by which she must act towards her patients in order to live up to the *reasonable man* test. If the nurse fulfills this duty, by acting in a reasonable manner, she is not negligent and is not liable to the patient, even if there is an injury. Perhaps the best way to understand the standard of care is by reviewing some actual cases.

In the use of drugs a Canadian court[1] held that the nurse has the duty to handle drugs with such care that harm will not result to those who depend upon her skill, and she must exercise reasonable skill to avoid such harm. Notice that the court ends up with the test of whether the nurse acted "reasonably." Other courts have established the same test by stating that a nurse is required to exercise ordinary or reasonable care to see that no unnecesary harm comes to her patients.[2] Many courts draw an exact analogy between the nurse and the physician, and state that the same tests of reasonable care are applicable to the nurse as to the physician.[3]

The physician must act like a reasonably prudent physician and the nurse must act like a reasonably prudent nurse.

Expert Witnesses

The jury or the court determines whether or not the nurse acted in a reasonable manner by referring to *expert witnesses* who testify as to what is reasonable and what unreasonable under the circumstances. There is a separate chapter on the nurse as an expert witness and the discussion at this point will be limited to describing the method the expert witness uses to establish the standard of care.

The expert witness qualifies as an expert by demonstrating that she has expert knowledge because of advanced training, extensive experience, or both. She testifies about what is reasonable, and not necessarily about what the best nurse would have done under the circumstances.

Consider the case in which a nurse went out to lunch before the doctor returned, leaving an unconscious child in the doctor's office. An experienced nurse testified as an expert witness and stated that under such circumstances standard nursing procedure would require the nurse to notify the physician and remain with the child until he arrived.[4] She also testified about the procedures that the reasonable nurse would have performed under the circumstances of this case.

Naturally, the nurse testifying as an expert witness on nursing is not qualified to testify regarding the standard of care required of a doctor in the practice of his profession.[5] However one court did state that a graduate nurse with many years of experience was qualified as an expert witness to testify as to whether an infant would have died of a disease had he not died of burns.[6]

Expert witnesses are not needed in all cases. If the conduct under question constituted part of the nurse's ministerial or nonprofessional activities, especially when in an area in which laymen could completely evaluate the conduct, there is no need for expert witnesses. This is one of the important reasons why the distinction must be made between malpractice and negligence, since the expert witness may be needed for the former, but not for the latter.

There was a classic case in Delaware[7] which brought up the interrelation of the standard of care and the need for an expert witness. An order sheet said a drug was to be administered orally rather than by needle, and the nurse used a needle with resulting injury to the patient. The court considered whether or not an expert witness was needed to establish the nurse's negligence, and stated, "ordinarily evidence of the required skill and care exercised by a nurse, generally should come from experts." However, in this case it was held that there was evidence to take the case to the jury without the aid of expert witnesses. The court described the duty of care that the nurse owes the patient, by stating that in the performance of her professional duties a nurse is required to exercise ordinary or reasonable care to see that no harm comes to the patient, and found that the nurse used less than ordinary or reasonable care in this case.

Under some circumstances the courts will dispense with the need for expert witnesses even in questions of professional competence, if the lay jury is considered competent to evaluate the nurse's conduct. This is demonstrated by two recent decisions in Michigan. Both cases involved the same defendant hospital and approximately the same fact situation. The question was whether or not the hospital nurse was negligent in attempting to assist a patient onto an examination table.[8] The courts held that the question was one of ordinary negligence and not malpractice, so that expert testimony was not necessary to show that the nurse violated or breached any duty required of a nurse.

Proof of Malpractice

In the discussion of negligence and malpractice the liability of the nurse is considered in situations in which the patient suffered a physical injury because of the alleged negligent conduct of the nurse either in doing an unreasonable act or in failing to do a reasonable one when required. These are the so-called *negligent torts*, in which the injury occurs without any overt desire that it occur.

Black's Law Dictionary defines a *tort* as:

> A private or civil wrong, or injury. A wrong independent of contract. A violation of a duty imposed by general law or otherwise upon all persons occupying the relation to each other which is involved in a given transaction.

Negligent conduct means the commission of a tort; malpractice is a tort committed while acting in a negligent manner in the course of professional services.

Any time one person injures another through his own negligent conduct, a tort is committed. One way to understand a tort is to contrast it to a crime. A crime is punishable by legal action brought against an individual by a governmental unit. A crime is the violation of some statute that states that certain conduct (e.g. murder) is prohibited, and provides some penalty against the individual who commits the crime. The penalty for committing a crime is a jail sentence or a fine payable into the public treasury. Although other individuals may be complaining witnesses in the case of a crime, they do not receive the money levied as a fine, nor do they get any other financial benefit arising out of the punishment for conviction of a crime.

The same action can give rise to a tort and a crime. For example, if a patient intentionally hits a nurse and knocks her down, he is guilty of a crime. He can be arrested and sentenced to jail or fined for his battery. However the jail sentence does not pay the nurse for the expense of medical attention or for the time lost from work due to the injury, so the nurse must bring a civil lawsuit against the patient to recover damages.

A legal action for a tort is a contest between an individual who has been injured and the individual who has caused the injury. It is a contest between two individuals and not between an individual and the state. When the injured party has won his lawsuit based upon a tort he is entitled to a legal judgment in an amount equal to his damages.

In a legal action against a nurse for malpractice there are three elements necessary to establish liability: there must be an injury, there must have been some negligent conduct, and the negligent conduct must have been the proximate cause of the injury. In most cases the burden of proof of all three elements is upon the patient.

Negligence and Injury

The fact that the nurse has been guilty of negligent conduct or malpractice does not establish legal liability to the patient unless the patient has suffered an *injury*. If the nurse has negligently administered the wrong drug with no resulting injury, because both drugs were equally effective or equally suitable to the situation, there is negligence but no injury. Therefore the nurse has no legal liability to the patient. The patient must prove that there has been an injury, and without doing so he cannot hope to recover a legal judgment against the nurse.

Proximate Cause

A nurse is not liable merely because the patient suffered an injury during the same afternoon that the nurse committed a negligent act. For the nurse to be held liable her negligence must have been the *proximate cause* of the injury, and in most cases it is incumbent upon the plaintiff-patient to prove proximate cause, although it need not be proven with absolute certainty.

Under some circumstances the courts will relieve the patient of this burden under the legal doctrine of *res ipsa loquitur,* which will be discussed in the next section. It suffices at this point to note that when *res ipsa loquitur* is applied there is no need for the patient to prove proximate cause, since it is established by the nature of the injury itself.

In a famous California case decided in 1949,[9] in which there was no specific evidence as to which of the particular defendant doctors or nurses negligently caused an injury to the patient's shoulder during an operation, the court found that the injury was the proximate result of the negligence of each and every one of the defendants. This case seemed to many legal authorities to be a major change in the law, because it appeared to dispense with the proof of proximate cause. Actually the decision assumed that the defendants all worked as a team, and stated that it would be improper to deny recovery to the patient merely because he could not show which member of the team actually caused the injury. The courts now seem to be following the trend towards saying that proximate cause is proved when any member of the health team could have caused the injury.

In a later California decision[10] the court considered the situation in which a patient suffered a third degree burn some time during the three day period after an operation. The court applied *res ipsa loquitur,* holding the nurse, doctor, and hospital liable even though the patient did not know how he received the burn. In another case a court held that where the wrong drug was injected the plaintiff did not need to show that the negligence of the nurse, doctor, or hospital was the cause of death, since the cause of death of the patient was presumed to be negligence.[11]

In other courts the judge will let the jury determine whether or not proximate cause has been proved. For example, a patient had cancer and a nurse had been negligent in permitting a foreign body to remain after an operation. The court said that this could have been the proximate cause and permitted a recovery against the nurse.[12] In another case it was alleged that a patient suffered gangrenous sores on her heels as a result of straps being applied too tightly to her feet during an operation. The court in this case said the question of proximate cause was for the jury to decide.[13]

Res Ipsa Loquitur

In some instances the plaintiff is not required to prove the nurse's negligence through expert witnesses, by application of the legal principle of *res ipsa loquitur* ("the thing speaks for itself"), which creates the presumption of negligence. The burden of proof is thus shifted from the plaintiff to the defendant, and in the absence of further proof the plaintiff is assured a favorable verdict. However, the presumption or inference of negligence is not absolute or conclusive; it is rebuttable and vanishes completely when there is even slight evidence to the contrary.

To secure the aid of *res ipsa loquitur*, the plaintiff must establish his injury and the background of facts that even, if unexplained, makes the inference of negligence permissible. The conditions usually necessary for the application of this doctrine are three: The accident must be of the kind that does not ordinarily occur in the absence of someone's negligence, it must be caused by an agent or instrument within the exclusive control of the defendant, and it must not have been due to any voluntary act or contributory negligence on the part of the plaintiff.

Not all states use this doctrine in malpractice cases, but the number is steadily increasing. When *res ipsa loquitur* has been held applicable in cases against nurses, the hospitals and physicians have also been named as defendants. It is likely, however, that in those states in which the doctrine is used by the courts, it will be applied even if the nurse is the only defendant.

Damages

After a patient has proved negligence, proximate cause, and resulting injury, and a verdict is reached against the nurse, the court or the jury returns to the question of "injury" to determine the amount of the judgment. In this context injury takes on a new meaning and is more properly considered as *damages*. In a malpractice suit, only the pain and suffering resulting from negligence are compensable in damages, and not that of the original injury. In most states the jury decides the amount of the judgment, and the court decides only whether or not the amount awarded is reasonable. Although the plaintiff has the burden of proving the injury and the damages, the mere fact that the plaintiff is unable to prove the exact damages does not relieve the nurse of liability. Because juries are known to be more generous than judges with the defendant's money, it is not surprising that plaintiffs usually prefer jury trials.

Punitive damages are also recoverable against a nurse when there is evidence that she was actuated by malice, or that she acted with recklessness, oppression, or with utter indifference regarding the effects of her acts. However few punitive actions are brought against professional persons on this basis.

References

1. Bugden v. Harbor View Hosp. 2 DLR 338 (N.S. 1947).
2. Larrimore v. Homeopathic Hosp. Assoc. 176 A 2d 362 (Dela. 1961).
3. Leonard v. Watsonville Community Hosp. 291 P. 2d 496 (Calif. 1956).
4. Crowe v. Provost, 374 S.W. 2d 645 (Tenn. 1963).
5. Crowe v. Provost, *supra.*
6. Longuy v. La Societe, 198 P. 1011 (Calif. 1921).
7. Larrimore v. Homeopathic Hosp. Assoc., *supra.*
8. Gold v. Sinai Hosp. 146 N.W. 2d 723 (Michigan 1966) and Fogel v. Sinai Hosp. 138 N.W. 2d 503 (Mich. 1965).
9. Ybarra v. Spangard, 208 P. 2d 445 (Calif. 1949).
10. Oldis v. La Societe, 279 P. 2d 184 (Calif. 1955).
11. Bugden v. Harbor View Hosp., *supra.*
12. Cooper v. Nat'l Motor Bearing Co., 288 P. 2nd 581 (Calif. 1953).
13. Palmer v. Clarksdale Hosp. 57 So. 2d 473 (Miss. 1952).

5   *Malpractice Actions Against the Nurse*

Suits Against the Nurse

THE RIGHT TO SUE.   In order to avoid legal claims against her the most the nurse can do in her everyday conduct is to live up to the test of reasonableness. If she possesses abilities beyond those required of her by law, she should feel bound to exercise these abilities. But no matter how reasonable or even perfect the nurse acts, there is no guarantee that she will not be sued for negligence or malpractice. When reference is made to preventing malpractice claims it is really in the sense of preventing successful malpractice claims and minimizing the chances that a lawsuit will be filed. Under the United States and Canadian systems of law anyone can file a lawsuit against anyone else if he feels aggrieved. The party sued has to defend the claim, no matter how spurious. The law provides some defenses against completely unfounded claims by early dismissal when it is obvious that there is no real possibility of liability.

WHO CAN BE SUED?   It is interesting to note that the malpractice claims against nurses and the claims against physicians and hospitals make no distinction between registered and practical nurses or between nurses and student nurses. In fact, the courts even blur the distinction between the nurse and someone who purports to act like a nurse for the purposes of determining whether or not any negligent conduct resulted in an injury to a patient. The cases really make no distinction between a trained or a registered nurse, a student nurse, or a practical nurse for negligence or malpractice charges.[1] It is clear that nurses of all types can be sued for their actions.

WHO CAN SUE?   Under our legal system any injured party can sue for the negligence that caused the injury. This does not limit the right to sue to the patient who was injured, although the patient is obviously the one who will bring the majority of lawsuits against the nurse.

The injured party can be a child's parent, who incurs future expenses because of the injury. The relatives of a deceased patient can sue for his loss. When the deceased was the head of the family, or the one supplying financial support for others, the dollar amounts of the claims can be very great. The injured party can also be the spouse of the patient who can sue for loss of comfort and companionship. A husband can sue for loss of services and for other financial expenses incurred because the wife is unable to perform housekeeping and similar functions.

When two or more persons sue for a physical injury the suits are usually combined into one case. For example, if a child is injured and sues for pain and suffering incurred because of the negligent conduct, and the child's father sues for the additional medical, hospital, and nursing expenses, both would be combined into one lawsuit.

Conceivably doctors or fellow nurses can sue the nurse for her negligence when they suffer a resulting injury, but here the question is of common negligence and not malpractice, and it would be no different than if the nurse had an auto collision with the other nurses or her employer. The nurse cannot sue her employer in most instances because of the operation of the workmen's compensation laws, which provide the sole means of redressing an injury suffered during a period of employment.

A recent and interesting lawsuit was filed by a nurse's husband against the physician who employed his wife. The husband sued on the basis that the doctor administered or made available to his wife narcotics that she used to her physical detriment. The husband sued the doctor for the loss of services of his wife, including loss of consortium. This case was scheduled for a new trial which apparently never took place. The subject reached the appellate courts when the doctor claimed as a business deduction the costs of defending the lawsuit brought by the husband. The Internal Revenue Service argued that the costs of defense were of a private nature and not deductible as a business expense. The doctor successfully convinced the court that the whole matter arose out of the practice of his profession, and that the deduction should be allowed as a business expense.[2]

WHEN TO SUE.   When a person has suffered an injury there is usually some time limit within which he must commence the legal action based upon that injury. This limit is established by the statute of limitations, which stipulates the time within which a plaintiff must bring his lawsuit, on penalty of losing his right to sue.[3] The rationale of the statute of limitations is that the negligent person should not be held in jeopardy for the remainder of his life wondering whether or not there will be a lawsuit filed against him. At some time in the future he should be able to relax and be safe from past conduct. The passing of time diminishes the opportunities to defend oneself, so the prospective defendant has a right to have the case against him brought within a reasonable period of time after the injury.

Generally a legal action based upon negligence or malpractice must be commenced within two years from the time the injury occurred. When the injury recurs, the two year period commences from the last injury. There is a separate statute of limitations for contracts; these suits may usually be commenced any time up to six years from the time the contract has been breached. There is an exception to the rule that the two year (depending on statute) period for suits based on negligence or malpractice commences from the time of the patient's last injury. When the doctor, nurse, or other person involved in the negligent act fraudulently conceals the injury, the time limit does not begin to run until the patient becomes aware or should have become aware of the injury.

Because the statute of limitations is an enactment of the state or provincial legislature the statutes vary from one jurisdiction to another. The nurse should be familiar with the statute of limitations in her own state, especially when she believes that there is a substantial chance that a malpractice or negligence lawsuit will be filed against her.

One of the important questions to the nurse is whether or not her conduct will be considered malpractice or ordinary negligence for the purpose of applying the statute of limitations. The distinction may be significant because the length of the statute may differ in the state between malpractice and common negligence actions. In 1929 a New York court considered this question.[4] New York had a two year statute of limitations for malpractice and a three year statute of limitations for common negligence. The patient was burned by a hot water bottle placed by a nurse and the legal action was commenced more than two but less than three years from the time of the injury. The court held that the term malpractice as it is used in the statute of limitations for malpractice cases has no application in the case of an injury caused by a nurse. This determination was crucial as the court was permitting the legal action to be started against the nurse.

In a more recent case in Ohio a negligence action was brought against a hospital, based on the doctrine of *respondeat superior*, for the alleged negligence of two nurses in permitting a patient to hemorrhage for eight hours, resulting in a transfusion from which she contracted hepatitis. Ohio had a one year statute of limitations for malpractice actions and a two year statute of limitations for other bodily injury cases. The Ohio court said that the negligence of the nurse was subject to the two year statute for bodily injury,[5] and also said that the statute of limitations was for physicians and not for nurses. This court held that the lack of due care by a nurse in caring for a hospital patient constituted ordinary negligence and not malpractice within the meaning of the statute of limitations. What makes the results in these two decisions vexing is the fact that both cases involved situations in which the nurses were performing professional rather than ministerial functions.

The majority of states do not have separate statutes of limitations for malpractice, and malpractice actions must be brought within the general statute of limitations prescribed for personal injuries. Seventeen states have a separate statute of limitations for malpractice, and all but five of these seventeen specifically state which persons are covered under this separate statute of limitations.

Common Grounds for Malpractice Actions

Perhaps the greatest benefit of a book of this nature is to make the nurse aware of the dangerous situations that can give rise to malpractice claims by pointing out some of the more common grounds for malpractice actions. The proper action in most instances, that is, what the nurse should have done to avoid a lawsuit, is a matter of good nursing practice rather than law. In many of these situations the nurse's legal duty will be clear if she stops to evaluate the situation and ask herself what the reasonable nurse would do under the same or similar circumstances. The discussion of common grounds for malpractice actions cannot include all possible situations from which malpractice claims may arise, but it can establish some general principles that are applicable in every situation.

Failure To Follow the Doctor's Instructions

Perhaps the single most common cause of malpractice claims against nurses is failure to follow the doctor's instructions, those cases in which the nurse did not understand the instructions and went ahead without contacting the doctor, and those in which the nurse knew what she was supposed to do but did something else instead. These are the most difficult cases to defend since it cannot be said that the nurse acted in a reasonable manner when she failed to contact the doctor or follow his instructions. The following cases will establish the pattern and the law.

In one case a fatal dose of the drug Lanoxin was injected in a three months old child. The nurse had been in doubt about the dosage but failed to call the physician, and the decision was against the nurse.[6] In another case the order sheet said a drug was to be administered orally instead of by injection and the nurse used a needle, with resulting injury to the patient. In this case the physician said that the nurse had made a mistake.[7] In the classic case in which the nurse in charge of the operating room did not read the label and supplied formalin instead of novocain,[8] the nurse was held liable for the resulting injury.

Drugs and Anesthetics

The injuries caused by drug and anesthetic agents have two things in common. They can be easily avoided and they often cause death. According to a report from the United States Public Health Service,[9] medication errors by nurses generally involve making mistakes in reading the doctor's orders, keeping drugs around after the patient for whom they were intended has left, and causing injuries to nerves in drug administration.

The failure to read labels continues to be an indefensible error. In a Canadian case a judgment in the amount of $10,000 was awarded against two nurses when they did not read the labels on the bottle one nurse handed to the other, and injected adrenalin instead of novocain.[10] The error committed when the nurse gives the physician the wrong drug is usually the nurse's, according to the courts. One court stated that the physician in an operating room with an experienced nurse acts properly in accepting instruments, medicines, and drugs from the nurse without examining them personally.[11]

The fact that the patient suffers injury from a drug or other agent does not necessarily mean that the nurse or the doctor is guilty of malpractice. If an unusual and unpredictable drug reaction occurs and the doctor had no prior reason to suspect the reaction, the courts will not hold the doctor or the nurse liable. Consider a recent case in Washington in which a nurse gave a child a penicillin injection as ordered by the physician. The nurse left the room and the patient was hurt when he fainted and fell on the floor. The court dismissed the action against the nurse on the basis that there was no proof of negligence or evidence of malpractice.[12]

Burns

Burns are some of the most common injuries occurring in a hospital. Nurses appear to have some propensity to place hot water bottles and other hot objects where they can cause serious burns to patients. Nurses, and especially student nurses, should be aware that if they place a hot water bottle at 212 degrees temperature on the patient's body, the patient will be seriously burned.[13] The nurse must understand that the hot water bottle ordered by the physician need not and should not be at the maximum possible temperature. Heat lamps are another source of burns to hospital patients. Nurses are well advised to consider that the reasonably prudent nurse never administers a water bottle so hot, or a heat lamp for so long, that burns are caused. The mere fact that there has been a resulting burn is often enough to show that the nurse has been negligent in performing her duties.

Infectious Diseases

The prudent nurse who has an infectious disease will always inform her superior in the hospital or the physician for whom she works, so that she will not come in contact with patients while there is a danger that she might communicate the disease to them. In a tragic case that presents the classic example of what should not be done, a nurse afflicted with tuberculosis was assigned by a hospital to attend a baby. The child later died of miliary tuberculosis. The hospital was held liable for permitting the nurse to attend babies while afflicted with an infectious disease.[14]

This does not mean that every time the patient alleges that he caught an infectious disease from the nurse she is automatically guilty of negligence, however. When one patient alleged that she caught a cold from a nurse, she was not able to recover a judgment against the nurse because she was not able to show that this was the cause of her pneumonia.[15] The same result occurred when it was alleged that a practical nurse having a boil caused an infant patient's injury. There was no indication of proximate cause and the plaintiff was unable to win the lawsuit against the nurse.[16]

In addition to her own personal hygiene the nurse has the responsibility to use clean instruments and to abstain from any conduct that may result in the spread of infectious disease. Even in these cases the burden is on the patient to prove that the infection resulted from some negligent act on the part of the nurse. In one case the patient alleged that he was injured by the nurse making a hypodermic injection at a place on the patient's skin that had not previously been sterilized. The court in this case found that there was nothing to show that an act or omission on the part of the nurse resulted in the formation of the abscess.[17] There was a similar ruling when a patient alleged that the nurse used an unclean catheter, causing the patient to contract cystitis.[18]

The nurse in the hospital or the private medical office has some duty to act in a reasonable manner to prevent the spread of disease among patients. In one hospital case the nurse brought the wrong baby to a mother for feeding and an infectious disease resulted in the mother. The patient was successful in her lawsuit against the nurse.[19] In this case there was proof that the baby brought to the mother was the carrier of the disease, and it was evident that the mother would not have contracted the disease if the nurse had not been negligent in bringing the wrong baby. Contrast this to a decision of the same court three years later, when it was alleged that the hospital nurse permitted one baby to infect another with impetigo. The court in this case found that there was no evidence that the spread of the infectious disease was caused by any negligent conduct on the part of the nurse.[20]

The fact that so many court decisions involving infectious diseases are in favor of the nurse and the hospital can be misleading. If there is an obvious cause and effect relationship between the nurse's conduct and the resulting injury, the case will usually not go to court, because it is indefensible. The cases that do go to court and result in a verdict against the patient, involve cases in which an infection is suffered by the patient and he cannot prove that the nurse's negligence was the cause of the infection. This should provide some measure of assurance to the nurse that she will not be found to be negligent every time a patient suffers an infectious disease. The patient must prove cause and effect.

Falls

According to one report[21] the shortage of nurses throughout the country may account in part for some accidents to patients. According to this report, upwards of 500,000 accidents occur annually in hospitals, and 46% of these involve falls from beds. However, there are not 240,000 claims filed each year against nurses and others for hospital bed falls, and it is obvious that the vast majority of these falls result from something other than the negligence of nurses and other hospital employees. When a nurse's negligent conduct does result in a fall, there is the serious question of legal liability. If the nurse permits the patient to leave the bed when he should not, or if the nurse does not provide enough support for the patient being helped to walk, the nurse will probably be found liable for the injury resulting from a subsequent fall.

Sponges and Instruments

"Lost" sponges and instruments after an operation present a complex problem, not in determining whether someone was negligent but in determining whose negligence caused the injury. When a student nurse participates in an operation and has no responsibility other than to pass sponges, she is not liable if she had no responsibility for maintaining the count of the sponges.[22] In one case a student nurse had the responsibility for counting the unused sponges, but the supervisor was held liable, since she had the responsibility of counting the used sponges and reported the count as correct before the incision was closed.[23] When the physician assigns a counting function to a nurse, however, this does not relieve him of the responsibility of assuring himself that no sponges are left in the patient.[24]

Nurses participating at an operation are each liable for their own negligent conduct in failing to act in a reasonable manner. When a supervising nurse assigned a nurse to an operation and the assigned nurse left a needle in the abdomen after an operation, the court held that the supervisor was not liable for the assignment.[25] The supervising nurse would probably be liable only if she makes an assignment knowing that the assigned nurse is not capable of meeting her responsibilities.

Diagnosis by a Nurse

One of the easiest bad habits a nurse can fall into is diagnosing patient's ailments. The fact that there have been so few legal actions brought against nurses for diagnosing is a tribute to the nursing profession.

The most famous case of a nurse being held liable for making a diagnosis involved a male industrial nurse with more than 30 years experience. The nurse diagnosed an illness as a virus condition and the patient died of a coronary occlusion a few hours later. In the court's words, this was "gross negligence," in that the nurse failed to notice symptoms that indicated a heart ailment requiring prompt treatment by a physician.[26]

The only other case found on this subject also involved an industrial nurse, whose own testimony established that the standard of care for nurses in the community required that a puncture wound be probed for foreign bodies. The court found that this nurse violated her duty to refer the patient to a physician for diagnosis of a condition with which she was not familiar, and about which she had some doubts.[27]

Two cases concerning nurses who were working for dentists involved situations in which the nurse substituted her judgment for that of the doctor, or merely forgot to report information to the doctor. In one case involving the extraction of teeth, the patient contended that the dentist was liable for the failure of the nurse to report the patient's statement that foreign matter had passed down her trachea. The nurse had informed the patient that this was "the natural thing after the extraction of teeth." In this case the patient sued the doctor. The court found that the nurse had no expressed or implied authority to give advice to the patient, and the doctor was not held liable for the statements of the nurse.[28] In this case it is likely that the patient would have been successful if he had brought the legal action against the nurse instead of against the doctor. In the second case the question was whether or not a dentist was bound by a message given to a nurse. The message stated that the dentist was needed for a house call. This court held that if the nurse had actual or ostensible authority to receive a message for the dentist, the dentist was bound by the message.[29]

Summary

The cases and situations discussed in this chapter are not all-inclusive. They obviously do not represent all the lawsuits filed because of the alleged negligence of a nurse, nor do they represent all the fact situations that can give rise to malpractice claims. Because the legal principles involved in malpractice cases are so well established, the vast majority of malpractice claims never reach the higher courts; in fact most of them never get into the courts in the first place. Only the appealed cases are recorded and freely available to report. The few cases that go to appeal are those that concern unique fact situations, or those in which there is a serious disagreement as to the facts.

From the cases discussed we can obtain a number of general rules for the nurse to follow:

1. The nurse must follow the doctor's instructions unless it is apparent that an injury to the patient will result.

2. If the nurse is in doubt about the doctor's instructions she should get the instructions clarified before she proceeds.

3. The nurse must read labels on bottles and not assume that she is using the correct drug or agent unless she is absolutely certain.

4. The nurse has the responsibility of making sure that the heat she is applying to the patient is not so great that it will result in a burn.

5. The nurse suffering from a communicable illness has the duty to inform the doctor who employs her or her supervisor in the hospital.

6. The nurse has the responsibility to provide reasonable safeguards so that patients in her custody will not fall.

7. The nurse participating in the operating room should fully understand her responsibilities with respect to sponge and instrument counts. She should know the duties assigned to her and not hesitate to speak out if she believes that there have been errors in the counts.

8. The nurse should refrain from diagnosing in every instance.

9. The nurse must faithfully report all messages from patients to the attending physicians.

10. The nurse should not substitute her judgment for that of the doctor.

References

1. See 51 ALR 2d 971.
2. Finger v. United States, 257 F. Supp. 312 (1966).
3. See 74 ALR 1256.
4. Isenstein v. Malconson, 236 N.Y.S. 641 (1929).
5. Richardson v. Doe, 199 N.E. 2d 878 (Ohio, 1964).
6. Norton v. Argonaut Ins. Co., 144 S. 2d 249 (La. 1962).
7. Larrimore v. Homeopathic Hosp. Assoc., 176 A. 2d 362 (Dela. 1961).
8. Hallinan v. Prindle, 62 P. 2d 1075 (Calif. 1937).
9. Legal Aspects of Public Health Service Medical Care. U.S. Public Health Service, Bethesda, 1967, p. 55.
10. Bogden v. Harbor View Hosp., 2 D.L.R. 338 (N.S. 1947).
11. Hallinan v. Prindle, *supra*.
12. Stafford v. Hunter, 401 P. 2d 986 (Washington 1965).
13. Benedict v. Bondi, 122 A. 2d 209 (Pa. 1956).
14. Taaje v. St. Olaf. Hosp., 271 N.W. 109 (Minn. 1937).
15. Hurley v. Nashua Hosp. Assoc., 191 A. 649 (N.H. 1937).
16. Thompson v. Methodist Hosp., 367 S.W. 2d 134 (Tenn. 1962).
17. Sheehan v. Strong, 154 N.E. 253 (Mass. 1926); also Posthuma v. N.W. Hosp., 267 N.W. 221 (1936).
18. Moses v. St. Borneabas Hosp., 153 N.W. 128 (Minn. 1915).
19. Kirchoff v. St. Josephs Hosp., 260 N.W. 509 (Minn. 1935).
20. Stone v. Lutheran Deaconess Hosp., 280 N.W. 178 (Minn. 1938).
21. "Lawsuits show need for Better Nursing," *Modern Hospital,* 103:104, July 1964.
22. Piper v. Epstein, 62 N.E. 2d 139 (Ill. 1945).
23. Piper v. Epstein, *supra*.
24. Davis v. Keer, 86 A. 1007.
25. Bowers v. Olch, 260 P. 2d 997.
26. Baur v. Mesta Machine Co., 176 A. 2d 684 (Pa. 1961).
27. Cooper v. Nat'l Motor Bearing Co., 288 P. 2d 581 (Calif. 1953).
28. Wintersteen v. Semler, 255 P. 2d 138 (1952).
29. Rising v. Veatch, 3 P. 2d 1023 (1931).

6   *Legal Responsibilities of the Nurse*

Following the Doctor's Instructions

In some ways the nurse has a greater problem than the doctor or the hospital in determining her legal responsibilities. The prudent man test can be applied to determine whether or not the doctor is negligent in his own conduct, and the legal doctrine of *respondeat superior* may be used to determine whether or not he is liable for the conduct of his employees. Under *respondeat superior*, which will be discussed more fully in Chapter 7, an employer is legally liable for an employee's negligent conduct occurring in the furtherance of the employment relationship. When the doctor has the right to direct and control the actions of the nurse, he can be held liable for her negligence in the performance of her duties. The nurse is not, however, relieved of her own legal responsibility and liability to her patient merely because she acts under the direction and control of the physician.

To the extent that the nurse must act in a reasonable manner and there is little she can do to control the application of *respondeat superior*, her situation is similar to the doctor's. The difference lies in the nurse's legal responsibility to follow the directions of the doctor. When must the nurse follow the doctor's instructions without question, when does the law require the nurse to act contrary to the doctor's orders, and when does the law permit the nurse to use her own judgment in the absence of the doctor? These are some of the most complicated legal questions presented to the nurse.

RESPONSIBILITY FOR FOLLOWING INSTRUCTIONS. The nurse who follows the doctor's lawful directions without reason to suspect that the patient will be injured thereby does not incur any personal liability to the patient. If the reasonably prudent nurse would follow instructions without question, every nurse is protected in doing so. However the fact that the nurse is following the doctor's instructions does not protect her from responsibility for her own actions if she negligently carries out the instructions with resulting injury to the patient.[1]

DUTY TO FOLLOW INSTRUCTIONS. As a general rule, the nurse must execute the orders of the physician diligently, unless the order is such as to lead a reasonable nurse to anticipate that harm will come to the patient from the execution of the order.[2] Another court described the duty of the nurse to diligently execute the orders of the physician in charge of the patient unless the order was such as to lead a reasonable person to anticipate that an injury would result from its execution.[3] If the nurse has no reason to question the doctor's orders, she is protected in carrying them out. If the nurse has some doubt about the doctor's orders she obviously has a duty to contact the doctor to ascertain his instructions.

DUTY NOT TO FOLLOW INSTRUCTIONS. To the duty to follow instructions there is a corollary duty not to follow instructions. If the nurse has reason to believe that the execution of the doctor's instructions will result in an injury to the patient, she has a legal duty not to carry out the instructions. It is obvious that she is not in the position to be second-guessing the doctor or substituting her judgment for his. If she does alter his instructions because she believes he is wrong, and there is a resulting injury to the patient, then the nurse is clearly negligent since she could never demonstrate that she had acted in a reasonable manner in changing a doctor's instructions when such change resulted in an injury to the patient.

If the nurse believes that there is some serious question about the doctor's instructions, she is legally bound to contact the doctor. Consider the case in Louisiana in which the nurse was in doubt about the amount of the drug ordered. Instead of calling the physician to make absolutely certain of the dosage intended, she injected a fatal dosage in an infant.[4]

The same principle is true if the nurse is following the doctor's instructions and it becomes evident that new conditions have arisen or the instructions are producing results that are injuring the patient. Under these circumstances the nurse has a duty to stop the treatment and contact the doctor. A Florida court[5] held that it was a nurse's duty to discontinue injection of a saline solution after it became evident that it was adversely affecting the unconscious patient.

The major problem arises when the doctor directs the nurse and she knows that some injury to the patient will result. If she performs the task knowing the inevitable result, she is clearly negligent and perhaps as liable to the patient as the doctor who gives the careless order. The problem is complicated by the fact that the nurse is naturally reluctant to suggest to the doctor that he is wrong. This is not a true dilemma, however, because the choice is obvious when the nurse must choose between an injury to the patient and incurring the wrath of the doctor. The nurse must be cautious in her approach to the problem so that she does not prematurely question the doctor's judgment, but at the same time she must not be so cautious as to permit an avoidable accident to occur. The best means of presenting the issue to the doctor is a matter of public relations or psychology rather than law. However one recommended method is for the nurse to present the problem in the form of a question, rather than in direct criticism of the doctor's actions. The question permits the doctor to change his mind while allowing him to make the affirmative statement as to what should be done.

This question of disobeying the doctor's instructions is raised as a part of this general discussion and not to suggest that this has been a major problem for nurses.

If the physician fails to act, or acts in such a manner that the obvious result will be an injury to a patient, the nurse has the duty to call this to the doctor's attention. When the attending physician fails to act the nurse has the duty to advise hospital authorities, so that appropriate action can be taken.[6]

CRIMINAL ACTS. Although there have not been many prosecutions against nurses for carrying out directions of the physician that are contrary to law, the nurse should be aware of the problem. If the doctor directs her to commit an illegal act, for example in abortion or narcotics situations, the nurse has the legal responsibility to avoid the unlawful act. If the nurse knows that she is performing a criminal act then she will be liable for the act even if done under the direction and control of her employer-physician. This might be somewhat different if the only alternative to the criminal act is serious injury to a patient, in which case the act might not be considered criminal. If the nurse is unaware of the fact that she is participating in a criminal act in a situation where a reasonable nurse would not be aware of this fact, the law may find that the nurse following the directions of the physician is not personally liable.

Providing Medical Advice

It should be obvious to the nurse that if she purports to provide medical advice she will be engaged in the unlicensed practice of medicine. However, there is the more subtle problem of providing medical advice without being conscious of this fact, which may result from the way in which the nurse makes some statement to the patient, or from the failure of the patient to appreciate the fact that the nurse is not providing total and complete advice.

She should also guard her speech to make sure she does not speak in such an ambiguous manner that her statements could be relied upon by the patient as medical advice. The nurse should be mindful of the fact that patients tend to take the nurse both literally and seriously when she speaks.

The patient in the hospital or in the doctor's office may not be as familiar with the relative distinctions between medicine and nursing as the nurse. The patient may give the nurse information and then decide that this information is unimportant because the nurse fails to react. Through no fault of the nurse, the patient later fails to disclose the information to the doctor, or otherwise relies on the nurse's silence. In such a case the nurse should tactfully inform the patient that the information should be presented to the doctor.

Avoiding Malpractice Claims Against Doctors

There appears to be ample evidence that there is a substantial increase in the number of malpractice claims brought against physicians. The costs of defense, amount of out of court settlements, and the jury awards have increased to such a point that malpractice and fear of malpractice lawsuits play a very important part in medical practice. The nurse who works under the direction and control of a physician does not have any legal liability for his negligent acts. However she does have a legal and moral duty not to act in such manner as to encourage malpractice claims against the physician.

The purpose of this section is to suggest to the nurse ways that she can assist her doctor-employer in reducing his potential exposure to claims of malpractice. If the doctor commits some obvious act of malfeasance that results in an injury to the patient, the most the nurse can do is attempt to retain as much of the good will as previously existed in order to reduce the chances of legal action. This section will include suggestions for discouraging lawsuits and especially suggestions for not encouraging lawsuits. It is in the latter instance, the avoidance of inadvertent encouragement of a lawsuit, that presents the nurse with the greater challenge.

Commenting on the Doctor's Services

A nurse should avoid commenting on the professional services performed by the doctor, since this is not her function and is obviously outside her area of professional competence. If the nurse makes some adverse comment to the patient (or to any person) concerning the professional services performed by the doctor, she has definitely breached her legal obligations to the doctor. The adverse comment made to the patient may be taken by the patient to mean that the nurse is encouraging the patient to seek legal recourse or further medical services from another doctor. Adverse comments about the doctor's services made to third parties may have a way of getting back to the patient and may encourage the patient to sue the doctor.

The nurse who believes that she is competent to review and evaluate the doctor's professional services is a dangerous person in a medical office, and the doctor would be well advised to dispense with her services. If the nurse believes that the doctor is grossly incompetent or otherwise provides inferior medical services, her obligation is to terminate her employment relation. Reporting the doctor to the Board of Medical Examiners is an extreme action that the nurse should not take lightly, but it may be warranted in certain instances.

Even if the doctor has been guilty of some gross error, the nurse is obliged to refrain from offering her comments. Even if she believes that the patient has serious grounds for legal action against the doctor, she has no right to suggest this to the patient. If the error was an obvious one and the patient can be expected to bring legal action, the nurse need not feel any obligation to supply information or otherwise participate in the legal battle, since her testimony will be elicited by the contenders in the legal proceeding. It is interesting to note that a nurse who feels compelled to advise a patient in this manner takes upon herself the practice of two professions in addition to nursing. First, she presumes to act like a physician in determining whether or not the doctor is acting properly, and second, she presumes to act like an attorney in evaluating the legal significance of the patient's injury. The nurse should avoid both courses of action.

Some difference of opinion exists about whether or not the nurse should make favorable comments to the patient concerning the professional services performed by the doctor. On one hand the nurse may be creating good doctor-patient relations. On the other hand she may be establishing herself as a critic of the doctor's professional abilities and the patient may become accustomed to her comments. Consider the nurse who always comments favorably each time the patient returns for a series of treatments and then one day fails to make the favorable comment. A sensitive patient may take the failure to comment to mean that the nurse has nothing good to say.

Error or Clinical Fact

When there has been an injury in the doctor's office, or even in the hospital, the nurse should avoid commenting on the nature of the injury or how it was caused, since this is not her role. If the nurse is asked a direct question, her response should always be a statement of clinical fact rather than a statement of cause. For example, if the nurse must speak at all, it is better for her to say "There is a puncture" rather than "The doctor punctured." In one instance she is making a statement of clinical fact and in the other she is evaluating the doctor's conduct. Although both statements should be avoided, it is definitely worse for the nurse to make an evaluation of the doctor than an evaluation of the injury. The nurse's statement at the time of injury is referred to as *res gestae*, a part of the incident, and the patient can later repeat this statement in court as evidence against the doctor.

Calming the Patient

From the legal standpoint there is little that can be said of the nurse's responsibility to calm the patient after injury has occurred. If the nurse possesses those fine qualities of being able to relax people and calm their anxieties, she is of particular value to the doctor. Many people are still sympathetic to the doctor, in spite of the large number of malpractice lawsuits. If the doctor and his nurse are able to recapture the patient's good will after an injury has occurred, it may go a long way towards minimizing the chances of a malpractice lawsuit. However this gets into a nonlegal area, so little can be added except the general suggestion that the nurse assist as much as possible in recapturing the patient's good will (if this is possible) after the injury.

Malpractice and Insurance

Some writers state that in most cases someone other than the patient usually suggests the malpractice suit. Sometimes the suggestion is unavoidable, especially when the injury results from obviously negligent conduct. Here there is nothing that the nurse can do to assist the doctor, but at least she should do nothing to increase his chances of being sued.

The reference to the doctor's failure to be sued for malpractice in prior years is one of the easiest ways to encourage a lawsuit. The word malpractice should not even be in the nurse's vocabulary when she addresses the patient. The nurse who suggests to the patient, "This really is not malpractice, you know," may be putting the word "malpractice" into the patient's mind for the first time. The nurse who makes the comment, "Dr. Smith has never been sued for malpractice," immediately after Dr. Smith has injured the patient, is guaranteeing that Doctor Smith's enviable record is going to be blemished. When the nurse says to the patient, "Dr. Jones has been in practice for 35 years without a malpractice lawsuit," she is guaranteeing that Dr. Jones will never make it to his thirty-sixth year without a suit.

The same silence that should apply to malpractice also applies to malpractice insurance. Under no circumstances should the nurse suggest to the patient that the doctor has malpractice insurance. The nurse should never answer the question, "Is the doctor insured?" with anything more than, "I do not know," followed by a rapid termination of this line of conversation. The nurse should never volunteer the information that the doctor is insured, nor should she answer any questions on this subject.

If the nurse volunteers the information that the doctor is insured any number of adverse results may ensue. The insurance company might argue that this voids the insurance agreement. The insurance company and the doctor might suggest that the nurse was conspiring with the patient against the doctor, and it could be argued that the nurse is encouraging lawsuits. In no event is it proper for the nurse to volunteer the information or comment on the fact that the doctor has insurance protection.

References

1. Wood v. Miller, 76 P. 2d 963 (Ore. 1938).
2. Norton v. Argonaut Ins. Co., 144 S. 2d 249.
3. Byrd v. Marion General Hosp., 162 S.E. 738 (N.C. 1932).
4. Norton v. Argonaut Ins. Co., *supra.*
5. Porrish v. Clark, 145 S. 848 (Fla. 1933).
6. Darling v. Charleston Community Memorial Hosp., 211 N.E. 2d 253 (Ill. 1965).

7   *Liability of the Doctor and Hospital for the Nurse's Actions*

Respondeat Superior

Perhaps one of the most important legal doctrines affecting the nurse's legal responsibility is the doctrine of *respondeat superior*, which states that an employer is legally liable for his employee's negligent conduct that occurs in the furtherance of the employment relationship. This principle applies to all master-servant situations.

The doctrine of *respondeat superior* applies to the nurse when she is acting under the direction and control of a physician or hospital. In any given case the question is raised and argued whether or not the right to direct and control the nurse exists. If in a given instance the hospital or doctor does have the authority to exercise direction and control over the nurse in the performance of her duties, the doctrine applies and the hospital or physician is responsible to the injured patient for injuries arising out of the nurse's negligent conduct. This is known as vicarious liability.

When a court awards a judgment in favor of a patient this stands as a court order against the person sued to pay the judgment. But what good is a court order or a judgment against a nurse in the amount of $100,000 when the nurse has only a few dollars in the bank and will probably not be able to pay much of this during a lifetime of work? It is obvious to the patient that the doctor and the hospital are more likely to have the funds to pay the judgment, if for no other reason than that they usually have insurance against malpractice claims. Thus from the nurse's point of view the doctrine affords some measure of protection against having to pay judgments or damages to a patient whom she has injured, since the injured person will usually sue the nurse's employer in the same lawsuit, making the nurse, the doctor, and the hospital defendants in one lawsuit. In some instances the patient does not even sue the nurse, and the lawsuit is filed against her employer.

The doctor's malpractice policy usually provides coverage for lawsuits brought against him for the negligent acts of his employees. Although the doctor's insurance usually does not afford any direct protection for the employee, in the usual office situation in which the nurse has allegedly injured a patient, it is likely that the courts will find that the employment relation existed (ability to direct and control) so as to make the doctor liable for the nurse's negligent conduct. In the hospital there is always the legal question of who the nurse was working for at the time of the injury. Naturally the insurance companies representing the doctor, the hospital, or both, will want to avoid paying claims based upon the nurse's actions, and this can be done if they can establish that the nurse was not an employee at the relevant time.

Although the doctrine of *respondeat superior* gives an injured person someone else to sue, it does not immediately relieve the negligent employee of his legal responsibility. The fact that a nurse is acting under the direction and control of a physician does not relieve her from her responsibility and liability to her patient,[1] and she should not feel that she is free to treat her patients with reckless abandon. Situations have arisen where the doctor and the hospital have been able to escape liability and the only one left to defend the case was the nurse.

It should be remembered too that the doctrine of *respondeat superior* is not dependent on salary, but rather on the ability of the employer to direct and control. When the nurse is acting independently of direction there may not be any employer liable for her actions. The best example of the nurse working without an employer is, of course, the private duty nurse.

There are also the nonlegal consequences of the nurse's actions. In addition to the unnecessary injury to the patient it may be expected that the doctor or hospital found liable for the nurse's actions will be less than pleased with her. It is likely that her employment will be terminated or that she will suffer a setback in her professional career.

The doctrine of *respondeat superior* works two ways, that is, the nurse could be the employer liable for the negligent acts of her employees. Again, it should be noted that the test of employment is not who pays the salary but rather the ability of one person to direct and control another. The nurse could have supervisory authority over other nurses or other persons, and her authority to direct and control their actions could result in *respondeat superior* making her liable for their actions. In one case, a nurse left a needle in the patient's abdomen after an operation. The supervising nurse was not held liable for making the assignment of the negligent nurse to the operation, since she was not held negligent in making the assignment.[2] A supervising nurse can be held liable for negligent acts in making assignments, but the liability would probably be based on the failure to make a proper assignment rather than on the basis of *respondeat superior*. As one report says, it is a basic responsibility of a nursing supervisor to determine whether a patient's needs can be trusted to someone else, and whether or not the nurse assigned is competent to handle them alone.[3]

Liability of the Physician

The doctor is liable for the nurse's actions only when he has the authority to direct and control them. Consider a recent case in Louisiana. A nurse visited a doctor on a personal matter and then drove home to another city where she worked and resided. As a favor she agreed to take a tissue specimen to the hospital in her home town. The nurse struck a pedestrian with her car on the way home and a lawsuit was filed against the doctor. The court said that the doctor was not liable for the negligent driving of the nurse, because he had no direction and control and she was not acting in furtherance of an employment relationship—no employment relationship existed at the time of the accident.[4] In the more common case in which the doctor sends a nurse on an errand and she uses either his car or her own, most courts would say that the doctor has direction and control and is therefore liable for the negligent driving of the nurse. If the nurse is commuting to work most courts would say the doctor is not liable for her negligent driving. If she has an errand to run for the doctor on the way to or from work, some courts might say that this is part of her employment. Others would say that the doctor is liable if the errand causes her to deviate from her normal route. The reason for mentioning this case is two-fold. It illustrates the fact that any action on the part of the nurse, whether professional or not, could give rise to liability on the part of the doctor, but his liability is limited to situations in which the nurse acted in the course of the employment relationship.

When the nurse is working in a private office it is likely that every act that she performs in furtherance of the doctor's practice will invoke the operation of *respondeat superior*. It is not a case of whether or not the doctor actually exercises his right to direct and control the nurse; the key question is whether or not he has this right.

When the nurse accompanies the doctor to a hospital to assist him, it is apparent that the rule of *respondeat superior* follows them into the hospital. However when the doctor avails himself of a hospital nurse to assist him, the question of his liability for her negligent conduct becomes more complex. Generally the doctor is not liable for negligent acts of hospital employees that are merely custodial or ministerial. Persons performing their hospital functions remain under the direction and control of the hospital and they are not the doctor's employees for the purposes of applying *respondeat superior.*

When the hospital nurse is "loaned" to the doctor and the hospital surrenders the right to give her direction and control, the nurse becomes the employee of the doctor for purposes of applying *respondeat superior,* even though for all other purposes she is considered to be an employee of the hospital. Some of the older cases said that the doctor was not liable for the nurse's actions even if the doctor had the right to direct and control the nurse, if the doctor did not own or control the hospital.[5] However more recent decisions do hold the doctor liable when he has the right to direct and control.

From the hospital's point of view, when direction and control is surrendered to an operating surgeon, the nurse ceases to be the hospital's employee for the purpose of applying *respondeat superior.* According to one authority, however, the courts in Canada, New Jersey, and Massachusetts have held that the nurse is an independent contractor,[6] and does not temporarily become the agent of the doctor during an operation, so that the doctor is not liable for the nurse's negligent acts. The majority of the jurisdictions take the opposite view.

Consider the following two court decisions for some insight into the question of whether or not the hospital has surrendered direction and control. In one case a hospital nurse was giving heat lamp treatments to a patient for bed sores, and in another the nurse was putting a hot water bottle on the patient's foot during an operation. Both cases resulted in burns to the patients. In the first case the court held that the nurse was performing a merely ministerial act for which the hospital and not the physician was liable.[7] In the second case the court found that the hospital had surrendered direction and control to the physician so the physician and not the hospital was liable for her negligent conduct.[8] There may not appear to be any difference between these two cases, since they admittedly come close to the gray area where it is difficult to determine who has direction and control. In cases such as these the patient will most likely sue the doctor, the hospital, and the nurse, and then each of them will try to escape liability.

Liability of the Hospital

The hospital as an employer is liable for all of the acts of its employees. This includes responsibility for all of the custodial and ministerial acts of hospital employees resulting in injuries to patients. Whenever it is clear that the patient was injured because of the negligent acts of any hospital employee, the liability of the hospital is established. The most common accident, the patient falling out of bed, usually results in hospital liability when it can be shown that this accident arose out of some negligent act of a hospital employee.

The liability of the hospital ends when the hospital surrenders direction and control to a visiting physician who is not an employee of the hospital. Naturally the physician can be expected to allege that the nurse was performing a ministerial act and the hospital can be expected to allege that direction and control was surrendered. It should be noted in this context that it is the insurance companies representing the doctor and the hospital that make these allegations, and not the doctor or the hospital administrator.

The doctrine of charitable immunity, which will be discussed in a later section, can combine with the failure of the hospital to surrender direction and control to eliminate both doctor and hospital from liability. In one case, a nurse in charge of an operating room supplied formalin instead of novocain to a physician. The California court held that the physician was not negligent because he was entitled to rely on the nurse for supplying instruments, medicines, and drugs as requested without examining them personally. The court found that supplying drugs was a ministerial function and *respondeat superior* did not apply. The hospital was not subject to suit because of the doctrine of charitable immunity then in force in that state. The nurse was found negligent for failing to read the label on the bottle and was the only one found liable to the patient.[9] Other courts might find that this was not a ministerial act and that the doctor was liable for the nurse's actions. The point here is that a situation can arise where the only one liable to the patient is the nurse. This is a reminder to the nurse that *respondeat superior* is not an absolute guarantee that someone other than herself will have to make financial restitution to the injured person.

Private Duty Nurse

The private duty nurse working in a patient's home is usually considered to be an independent contractor. The doctrine of *respondeat superior* does not apply since no one has the authority to direct and control the exercise of her professional functions, and she is the only one liable for her negligent conduct.

What about the private duty nurse working in a hospital? It is difficult at times to determine whether the private duty nurse in the hospital is acting under the direction and control of the physician or the hospital for the purposes of applying *respondeat superior*. It could be argued that the nurse is the agent of the patient because he hires her and pays her salary. It could also be said that the nurse is an employee or agent of the hospital if the hospital has a regular scheme for procuring private duty nurses for patients and controls the work of these nurses. Or it could be argued that the nurse is the agent or employee of the physician who procures her services. Each case must be resolved on its own facts by applying the test of the right to direct and control. There can be as many different decisions on this question as there are different situations under which special duty nurses are hired.

In one case it was said there was a question of whether the nurse was an agent of the physician or an agent of the patient, since she was hired by the patient but took some directions from the physician.[10] In another case the court held that the hospital is not liable for the negligent acts of the special duty nurse.[11] More often it will be a question of the physician's liability rather than hospital liability for the special duty nurse, since the physician is more apt to have some responsibility to direct and control her actions.

In New York a patient claimed that he gave his dentures to his special duty nurse in a hospital and the nurse claimed that the patient never gave her the dentures. The patient sued the hospital for his missing dentures. The question before the court was whether the special duty nurse was an employee for the purpose of applying *respondeat superior*. The court believed the nurse, and it really was not necessary to get into the question of *respondeat superior*, because if the nurse had not acted improperly the hospital could not be liable for her improper actions. In any event the New York court took this opportunity to comment on the application of *respondeat superior* to the special duty nurse and found that the nurse was engaged by the hospital at the request of the patient. The hospital paid the wages to the nurse and collected this amount from the patient when it collected all other charges. The court found that in this case the nurse was not the employee of the hospital. There was no report on the dentures, which have now been missing since 1940.[12]

There are times when the nurse may be acting as an employee of the hospital even though the hospital and the nurse do not consider that an employment relation exists. Consider the case in which two student nurses volunteered to provide private nursing services for an infant during their off-duty hours, free of charge. The child was very ill and needed private nursing care. It was wartime, there was an unusually bad shortage of nurses, and the parents were unable to get a regular private duty nurse, so the students asked permission of the head nurse to take on the assignment. The head nurse was against the idea of the nurses taking turns as special duty nurses each night while they were still students. She also considered the fact that state law set a limit on the number of hours a female could legally work each day. Finally she agreed because of the humanitarian aspect of the request. There was a fire and the question was whether the cause of the child's death was the fire or the disease from which he suffered. The parents sued the hospital under the doctrine of *respondeat superior*, alleging that the child died from the fire and the hospital was liable for the nurse's negligent conduct in not saving the child from the fire. The court found that the doctrine of *respondeat superior* applied in this case and rejected the argument that the two student nurses were independent contractors. The court found that when the hospital agreed to the student nurses doing as they planned, it amounted to an assignment to this special duty. Thus the hospital was liable under *respondeat superior* since it was exercising direction and control over the nurses.[13]

Summary

The nurse need not become an expert on *respondeat superior*, but she should be aware of the fact that someone else is usually involved in accounting for her negligent conduct. She should know that she is not free to require that the matter be between herself and the patient, since the patient has the legal right to look to her employer for his legal satisfaction. The nurse should be aware of the fact that this legal doctrine does give her a measure of legal protection, but that there are instances when she alone must account for her negligent acts.

Charitable Immunity

Earlier in this chapter it was suggested that the hospital may not be liable to the patient because of the doctrine of charitable immunity. To the nurse the impact of disallowing claims against the hospital under this legal doctrine could be very great, since it could leave the patient with no option but to look to the nurse for legal recompense.

The doctrine of charitable immunity, which provides that charitable and nonprofit hospitals cannot be sucessfully sued for damages, is disappearing. The law is changing very rapidly in this area and it is not unlikely that this doctrine will disappear completely before long. The law is also confusing on this subject, and there is substantial variance in the law from one state to the next. The divergence of the courts in applying the doctrine of charitable immunity is seen by the contrary decisions adopted by a Missouri court in 1966 and a North Carolina court in 1967. The Missouri court[14] said that the doctrine of charitable immunity bars a patient's suit against a hospital. The North Carolina court[15] said that a patient's suit against a hospital is not barred by the doctrine of charitable immunity, reaching an opposite result in virtually the same fact situations.

The underlying principle of charitable immunity is that the hospital exists by virtue of charitable funds, and if these funds are used to pay judgments in personal injury suits there will not be sufficient funds available for operating the hospital. There is also the rationale that the funds were donated to operate the hospital and not to give awards to injured patients. The idea here is that the hospital only holds the funds to be used for the purposes that the contributor intended, and it would be a breach of trust for the hospital to pay the money to the patient.

The doctrine does not evidence any lack of sympathy for the injured patient but rather indicates that the common good in keeping the hospital operating is more important than the injury to one patient. The doctrine of charitable immunity is statutory law and the courts appear to be dedicated to finding ways to avoid applying it. One way the statute has been amended by the courts is by determining that it does not apply when the doctrine of *respondeat superior* is applied. Another exception is when the hospital is sued for its negligent act in hiring or retaining an employee who is known to have a propensity to injure patients.[16]

A recent change in an Illinois law based on charitable immunity is worth noting, if for no other reason than to illustrate how the courts are attempting to change it. One Illinois court said that if a hospital purchased liability insurance there was no need to apply the doctrine of charitable immunity, since its application would protect the insurance company and not the hospital. The law in Illinois was that if the hospital was insured the doctrine was waived, and the waiver existed only to the extent of the insurance. This presented the anomalous situation in which the hospital could not be sued unless it had insurance, and if it was insured it could only be sued to the extent that it was insured. In 1965 the Illinois court finally overruled the doctrine of charitable immunity for hospitals and also said a hospital could be sued for the negligent acts of its employees without regard to insurance coverage.[17]

Theoretically, it could be stated that the nurse is better off working in a hospital and in a state where the doctrine of charitable immunity does not exist since the presence of this doctrine works against her. However, there has never been any substantial evidence that more nurses are sued or lose lawsuits when they are working in hospitals protected by charitable immunity than when they are working in hospitals that do not enjoy this protection.

Indemnification

When the patient calls the nurse, the doctor, and the hospital as potential defendants in a lawsuit arising out of the negligent actions of the nurse, it is likely that the patient will sue all three in one lawsuit. The patient can get judgments against all three defendants, but cannot collect against all three. For example, if the patient is awarded $1000 for an injury received in a hospital due to the negligence of a nurse, and the judgment is awarded against the hospital, the doctor, and the nurse, he can only enforce his judgment against any one of the three. When the defendants are represented by two or more insurance companies, the insurers will usually agree among themselves to contribute toward the judgment. If the hospital and the doctor are insured and the nurse is not, it is likely (but not certain) that the hospital and the doctor (actually their insurance companies) will share in paying the judgment. If the nurse is insured and she is represented in the case, then her insurance company will also contribute to the judgment.

In some cases the nurse might not even be named as a party to the case. The nurse may be the negligent one, but the patient may decide that he would rather bring the action against the doctor and the hospital, or either one. There could be any number of reasons why the nurse is not sued, not the least of which is the possibility that she cannot be found or that she has left the jurisdiction of the court. Once the patient has been paid, the legal liability of the nurse ceases.

If the hospital and the doctor are sued instead of the nurse and the patient loses the case, this may not prevent the patient from later bringing an action against the nurse. Theoretically the patient can keep instituting lawsuits until he has received a judgment, or until he has sued everyone involved and has lost in every instance. If one party makes an out of court settlement with the patient, this amount will be deducted, in most cases, from the judgment awarded. The patient may not recover more than the amount of his judgment.[18]

What if the doctor or the hospital has paid a judgment? Can they now sue the nurse to recover the funds that were lost because of her negligent conduct? Indemnification is generally allowed in favor of one who is held responsible solely by imputation of law because of his relation to the wrongdoer. If an employer is held liable for the negligent conduct of his employee, without regard to the employer's own actions, the employer is entitled to indemnification against the employee. The employer has vicarious liability, that is, liability without fault, so he has a legal claim against his employee to recover the loss.

This means that if a doctor has to pay a judgment solely on the basis of *respondeat superior* because of the negligent actions of his nurse, the doctor has the legal right to recover this amount from the nurse. It is not often a question of whether or not the doctor wishes to bring action against his nurse; it is the option of the insurance company that has paid the judgment awarded against the doctor.

If the doctor and the nurse each participated in the wrongful act, that is, if they are joint tortfeasors, the doctor's liability is not based upon *respondeat superior*, and he has no right of indemnification against the employee. However, if the doctor has paid the judgment, he has the right for contribution and he can get the nurse to share the loss.

If the doctor authorized the act that proved to be negligent he is directly at fault and is liable to the patient even if there was no employer-employee relation and the doctrine of *respondeat superior* did not apply. Here there is clearly no room for indemnification. From the nurse's point of view the question of whether the doctor is being sued for his independent act or whether he is being sued for the acts of the nurse under the doctrine of *respondeat superior* is crucial.

In a recent case a physician was found to be negligent in the selection of a drug. He alleged that the injury was caused by the negligence of the nurse in administering the agent, and later sued the nurse for indemnification. The court held that the physician was not entitled to indemnification since he was liable for his own negligent conduct and not merely on the basis of *respondeat superior*.[19]

It is surprising that so few actions against doctors and hospitals based upon *respondeat superior* result in indemnification suits against the nurse. Perhaps this is due to the reluctance of the insurance company to bring lawsuits against other liability insurers (the nurse's insurance company). One way to avoid the indemnification lawsuit is by the doctor and the nurse purchasing their malpractice insurance protection from the same insurance company. Some hospitals that carry malpractice insurance for responsibility under the doctrine of *respondeat superior* have additional coverage in the same policy for the hospital employees. In this instance there would be no sense to the hospital's insurance company bringing an indemnification lawsuit against the nurse since it would really be suing itself.

References

1. Wood v. Miller, 76 P. 2d 962 (Ore. 1938).
2. Bowers v. Olch, 260 P. 2d 997.
3. Legal aspects of Public Health Service Medical Care. U. S. Public Health Service, Bethesda, 1967, page 48.

4. Mohr v. Schmitt, 189 S. 2d 46 (La. 1966).

5. Hall v. Grosvenor, 267 Ill. App. 119 (1932).

6. C. L. Cusumano, Malpractice law dissected for quick grasping. New York, Medicine-Law Press, Inc., 1962.

7. Swigerd v. City of Ortonville, 75 N.W. 2d 217 (Minn. 1956).

8. Benedict v. Bondi, 122 A. 2d 209 (Pa. 1956).

9. Hallinan v. Prindle, 62 P. 2d 1075 (Calif. 1937).

10. Louxader v. James, 107 S.W. 2d 976.

11. Pivar v. Manhattan General Hosp., 104 N.Y. S. 2d 575.

12. Fisher v. Sydenham Hosp., 26 N.Y.S. 2d 389 (1941).

13. Longuy v. La Societe, 198 P. 1011 (Calif. 1921).

14. Koprivica v. Bethesda General Hosp., 410 S.W. 2d 84 (Co. 1966).

15. Rabon v. Rowan Memorial Hosp., 152 S.E. 2d 485 (N.C. 1967).

16. Rabon v. Rowan, *supra.*

17. Darling v. Charleston Community Memorial Hosp., 212 N.E. 253 (Ill. 1965).

18. Darling v. Charleston, *supra.*

19. Campbell v. Preston, 379 S.W. 2d 557 (Mo. 1964).

8 *Non-Negligent Acts of the Nurse Resulting in Liability*

When a nurse acts knowing that a specific result will occur and the consequence of this act is that a patient is injured, the nurse has committed a non-negligent tort. The intended result is not that the patient will suffer an injury, but nevertheless the event that caused the injury is one that the nurse intended to occur.

Fraud and Deceit

Perhaps the best example of a non-negligent tort that may also be a crime is fraud and deceit. A swindle, for example, is not a result of negligence, but rather of an intention that the actual result will ensue. For there to be fraud and deceit there must be something more than an individual getting a bad bargain. It must be clear that there was an intent to deceive. This is something more than the fact a swindler has misled his victim. In a given instance there may be a gray area between fraud and simple sharp dealing; one is a tort and the other is not. Because greater evidence is needed in a criminal case, the easier of the two actions to prove when an individual has been victimized is the civil action.

The only significant area in which nurses are accused of practicing fraud and deceit is when it is claimed that the nurse took advantage of her position and got the patient to make large payments or gifts, or amended a will in her favor. Most of these situations seem to arise in private duty nursing where the patient is old and very ill, and requires extensive care. Later the patient or his heirs underestimate the extensive duties performed by the nurse and allege that the payments she received resulted from fraud and deceit on her part. This is good reason for a private duty nurse to discuss her fees in advance with her patients or with the close relatives of the patient when it is apparent that the patient does not fully appreciate the nature of the services and the fees. This does not mean that every time the nurse accepts a present or a bonus from a patient she has practiced deceit. The burden is on the person alleging deceit to prove the tort. However, a large gift that is disproportionate to the services rendered may be some evidence of deceit when the patient's mental state is such that he is not capable of comprehending the nature of the gift he is making.

Libel and Slander

The laws pertaining to libel and slander rank among the most misunderstood laws. This might be expected because these are some of the most confused and apparently illogical laws.

Libel and slander are acts or means of defaming another. Sometimes the terms are used interchangeably, but there is a significant difference between them. Libel is a method of defamation expressed by print, writing, pictures, or signs. It is a publication that is injurious to the reputation of another. Slander is the speaking of defamatory words that tend to prejudice another's reputation.

The difficulty in this area of law is in proving what is defamatory, and this is complicated by the fact that certain defamatory statements are privileged or partly privileged. The newspaper account of an event and a critic's review of a play are good examples of possible defamatory statements that do not constitute torts because they are privileged.

The nurse undoubtedly has a qualified privilege to make defamatory statements about patients, either orally or in writing, to her supervisors when such statements are a necessary part of her nursing practice. The statements must be in the area of her responsibility, however, and they must be made in a professional communication to someone entitled to receive that communication. Contrast with this the following situations. The physician has examined the patient and is having difficulty with the diagnosis. The nurse suggests that she recalls that the patient was admitted two years ago for a venereal disease. In another situation the nurse calls her friend on the telephone to say that the patient was admitted to the hospital, and he had been admitted two years ago for a venereal disease. In the first instance the nurse undoubtedly had a legal privilege to disclose the information, while she had no legal privilege to do so in the second instance. If this oral communication had been overheard the patient would have had a good action in tort against the nurse for libel, regardless of whether or not the patient had really had a venereal disease.

Truth is not an absolute defense in all cases. To protect herself against claims of libel and slander the nurse should limit her comments about patients to statements of clinical fact to persons entitled to receive these comments.

The nurse may occasionally be the one in the position to bring legal action against another for libel and slander. Conceivably the action could be against a physician or a patient who has made a defamatory comment or written a defamatory statement about the nurse. Most actions against physicians however are unsuccessful if they arise out of professional practice, since the physician undoubtedly has a qualified privilege to comment upon the nurse's abilities to other physicians and nurses. The physician would have to go far outside the bounds of propriety to be guilty of libel or slander in such a situation. There are few recorded cases of a nurse bringing an action against a physician or patient for libel or slander.

False Imprisonment

There is a natural tendency to brush past this section and assume that because one does not engage in locking other people in rooms the question of false imprisonment has little relevance. However, there are too many situations in the medical office or the hospital that can give rise to this claim to ignore the problem. Whenever patients have been locked in medical offices, or have not been permitted to leave the office until they make some payments, or whenever patients are not permitted to get out of the dental chair until they agree to make payments, there have been resulting claims of false imprisonment.

False imprisonment is the unlawful detention of another for any length of time whereby he is deprived of his personal liberty. If the false imprisonment is negligent, that is, if the guilty party does not intend to detain the other but does so through negligence, then the action in tort is usually limited to actual damages. An example of a negligent false imprisonment is locking a patient in a medical office accidentally when the office is closed for the night. The intentional detaining of the patient would be non-negligent and the patient would be able to recover punitive damages. Most false imprisonment actions are based on non-negligent conduct.

Since false imprisonment applies only to unlawful detentions, if the detention is permitted by law there can be no legal action. For example, some states permit a store detective to detain for a reasonable period of time a customer who is suspected of having left the store without paying for goods, in order to ascertain whether or not there has been a crime. The test here is "reasonable period of time," and if the detention exceeds that period it becomes false imprisonment. In the medical office there are few opportunities to say that detention against the patient's will is lawful and it is likely that the patient so detained will be considered to have been falsely imprisoned.

A patient in a hospital presents another problem. Although physicians and nurses may customarily order patients to remain in the hospital, it is clear that the patient is not really being detained. If the patient insists on leaving the hospital even if it is contrary to good medical practice, the nurse or physician who restrains him may be guilty of false imprisonment. It is only when the patient is restrained for public protection or any other lawful purpose that the hospital has the right to restrain him, such as restraining an insane patient, a patient who is not capable of understanding the situation, or a patient suffering from an infectious disease when there is fear of contagion. Detaining a patient need not be by physical means to constitute false imprisonment. If the patient is threatened with physical violence, or placed in a position where he cannot leave without risking an injury, he has been sufficiently restrained for the action to constitute false imprisonment.

Technical Assault

Every individual has the legal right not to have his person touched by another without his consent. Touching another without consent is a violation of a legal right and could result in a lawsuit based upon the tort of technical assault. This should be distinguished from criminal assault, which is touching another while possessed with a particular frame of mind, usually with the threat or contemplation of specific injury. The discussion of technical assault bears no relation to criminal assault, since it does not involve any spurious motive on the part of the nurse.

The law implies consent to certain touchings. A tapping on the shoulder, or any of the many other everyday touchings, is not technical assault because the law implies consent to these common touchings. When a patient enters a doctor's office he consents to touchings necessary for a simple examination. The patient need not manifest agreement to these touchings, since his presence in the examination room implies consent. A touching in excess of or contrary to this constitutes a technical assault. It is the right of the patient to have an examination, diagnosis, and consultation, and thereafter it is for the patient to determine what, if any, treatment or operation should proceed.

Consider the situation in which the patient has entered an examination room and the doctor determines that an injection of some kind is necessary. If the nurse proceeds to give the injection without the patient's consent and surprises him, the patient may sue for a technical assault. The nurse is well advised to seek the patient's consent before administering any treatment. If the patient consents to treatment by the physician this may be sufficient consent for the nurse to act, if the procedure is commonly among those delegated to a nurse. However, the nurse should get in the practice of obtaining the patient's consent before any procedure. This can be done by a simple question, such as "Shall I proceed now?" or "Do you want the injection in the left or right arm?" Any indication from the patient that he wants the nurse to proceed constitutes consent. The nurse or doctor need not specifically ask, "Do you consent?"

The nurse should be aware that there are at least two classes of persons incapable of giving consent. Minors generally are not legally capable of consenting to medical or dental treatment, and consent from a minor is no consent. Unless there is an emergency, an operation or procedure performed upon a minor without the parent's consent is a legal wrong. The parent's consent need not be a formal written authorization; a phone call may suffice. When consent is unobtainable a doctor or nurse may be reasonably safe in treating a minor if the child is of reasonable maturity, and if the treatments are necessary. The other class of persons incapable of giving consent is persons suffering mental deficiencies. If the patient does not understand the nature of the operation and the risks involved, the consent received from him amounts to no consent.

When the patient is unable to give consent in an emergency situation the best thing to do is get consent from the closest adult relative. If this is not possible, consent will be assumed if a true emergency exists. The fact that it is inconvenient to get consent is not sufficient grounds on which to find that an emergency exists.

Invasion of Privacy

Every individual has a legally protected right to his privacy subject to the permission he gives others to make use of his name or photograph. The essence of the action in invasion of privacy lawsuits is not injury to the character or reputation (as in libel and slander), but direct wrongs of a personal nature resulting in injuries to the feelings, without regard to any effect that the communication may have on the standing of the individual in the community. A person who unreasonably and seriously interferes with another's interests in not having his affairs known to others or his likeness exhibited to the public is under a legal liability to the other.

A patient in a medical office or in a hospital retains his right of privacy. He has a right to insist that the doctors and nurses do not invade his privacy by making him or his medical condition a subject of unnecessary discussion or gossip. A nurse who gossips about patients will undoubtedly incur the wrath of the doctors and other nurses she serves. In addition, she is subject to a lawsuit by the patient for invasion of privacy. Clearly the right of the patient to sue is limited to unnecessary discussions of the patient, and does not include discussions for medical purposes.

When patients are to participate in clinical demonstrations they should be informed in advance and their consent obtained. The patient has a right to insist that he not be used as the subject of a demonstration. If the patient is to be photographed for a report, the patient should be asked to consent to the use of the photograph.

The nurse should follow the general rule that she has no right to violate the patient's privacy except when necessary to provide needed medical or nursing care.

9 *Negligent and Non-Negligent Acts of the Patient*

There are three general areas in which the negligent conduct of the patient effects the legal relations between nurse and patient: failure to follow instructions, contributory negligence, and negligence resulting in an injury to the nurse.

Failure to Follow Instructions

When the patient's injury results not from any negligent conduct on the part of the nurse but rather from the patient's own negligent conduct, the patient has no legal recourse against the nurse. Consider the situation of the nurse telling an apparently rational adult not to attempt to get out of bed by himself. The patient decides to test himself and is injured in the attempt to stand up. The nurse was not negligent and the sole cause of the patient's injury was his own failure to follow instructions. In this situation the court is apt to find in favor of the nurse, unless the nurse knew, or should have known, that the patient could not or would not follow instructions.

If a patient is told to return to the doctor's office or the hospital for further treatments and fails to do so, it is likely that the courts will find that the resulting injury was caused by the patient's failure to follow instructions, rather than negligent conduct on the part of the doctor or nurse. Refusal of treatment after a reasonable explanation as to its necessity, by an adult patient who is in possession of his faculties and capable of exercising free judgment in agreeing or refusing, is a complete defense for a doctor or nurse who is accused of negligence in not giving treatment.

In general, when the cause of the injury is the failure of the patient to follow reasonable instructions while he is mentally and physically capable of doing so, the result will be a finding that the patient's act was the cause of his injury and there will be no liability on the part of the doctor or nurse.

Contributory Negligence

It is the duty of a patient to use the care that a man of ordinary prudence would use in circumstances similar to his own. He usually cannot hold a doctor or a nurse answerable for the consequences of his own lack of ordinary care. For the negligence of the patient to constitute a bar to a malpractice suit against a nurse, it must have been an active and efficient contributing cause to the injury, simultaneous and cooperating with the fault of the nurse. The acts of a patient during or after treatment that contribute to or aggravate an injury constitute contributory negligence and in most states bar recovery from the doctor or the nurse.

Contributory negligence must be distinguished from the situation in which the sole cause of the injury is the negligent act of the patient. If the patient's negligent act is the sole cause of the injury, the nurse's defense in a malpractice suit is that she was not negligent. Contributory negligence is raised as a defense in a malpractice suit when the nurse or doctor may be willing to admit negligent conduct on their part, but allege that the patient was also negligent and that without the patient's contributory negligence the injury would not have resulted. The rationale behind the legal defense of contributory negligence is obvious. If the patient's negligence contributed to the injury then it would be unfair to hold the nurse solely liable for the injury, even though she was also guilty of negligent conduct.

Contributory negligence is called an affirmative defense. This means that if the nurse wishes to use the defense of contributory negligence to defend herself in a malpractice action, she must raise this defense. In addition, she must establish contributory negligence in the same manner that the patient must establish negligence. In some jurisdictions the defense of contributory negligence is available only if the nurse is willing to admit that she was negligent in the first place. In most jurisdictions, however, the nurse can defend herself in the usual manner and then state that even if she was negligent, which she does not admit, the patient was guilty of contributory negligence.

Practically speaking, the defense of contributory negligence is very seldom raised in nursing malpractice cases. This may be so because the nature of the nursing profession is such that the patient plays only a passive role, so that he does not have any opportunity to perform an act of contributory negligence. Naturally if the patient is unconscious or does not have control of his faculties at the time of injury, he cannot be guilty of contributory negligence. When the patient has been guilty of contributory negligence, the use of this as a defense is strictly in the hands of the attorneys defending the nurse. The reason for discussing it is to assure the nurse that the negligence of the patient will not be forgotten when she is being defended.

Negligence Resulting in an Injury to a Nurse

In addition to the patient's responsibility not to cause or contribute to his own injury, the patient has the legal obligation to act in a reasonable manner toward the nurse so as not to cause her injury. The fact that there is a relationship of patient and nurse does not insulate the patient from fulfilling this legal responsibility.

If the patient injures the nurse in the absence of any professional treatment, the usual tests are applied to determine liability, as if the relationship of patient and nurse did not exist. Examples of this would be knocking the nurse down, dropping things, pushing, and so forth, with resulting injury to the nurse.

If the nurse is providing a professional service at the time of injury, the situation is different. The court may say that the nurse has assumed the risk, and may deny recovery to the nurse on this basis. The rationale here is that the nurse knows that this particular kind of risk occurs in nursing practice and she agrees to assume that risk when she becomes a nurse. Assumption of risk would be a defense to claims against patients in some states but not in others. If the nature of the negligent conduct or the injury is of the sort that would be totally unexpected in normal nursing practice, the doctrine of assumption of risk would not apply.

Whether or not the doctrine of assumption of risk is applied, there is still the question of the patient's negligence. For example, consider the nurse who is assigned to a contagious diseases ward and contracts a disease from a patient. The patient in the ward was not negligent in transmitting the disease and the nurse has no right of recovery against the patient, without consideration of the assumption of risk question. If the nurse is injured while assisting a patient to walk when the nurse or the doctor suggested that the patient walk, it is doubtful that the nurse would be successful in a lawsuit against the patient. Under these circumstances the doctor or nurse may be negligent in suggesting to the patient that he walk too soon, or the nurse may be negligent in not getting assistance in walking the patient. If the patient falls through no fault of his own, it is likely that the patient would be considered not to be negligent, or the court might find that the nurse assumed this risk when she attempted to assist the patient in walking.

Assault and Battery upon the Nurse

Whenever one person physically injures another, the injured party has legal cause for action. Assault is commonly defined as the threat to do a battery. One person assaults another by threatening to do him physical violence. The physical violence then constitutes the battery. For a criminal proceeding against a patient the nurse must usually show that there was an intent to commit an assault and battery, but for a civil action for damages, showing intent is not usually necessary. This means that a person can be successfully sued for assault and battery even though he did not intend to injure the other person. If a patient commits assault and battery upon a nurse, she has the usual protection of the law and has recourse to criminal law enforcement. The patient may be arrested and jailed or fined. In addition the nurse may sue the patient for damages to compensate her for her injuries.

The problem becomes more complex when the patient was insane at the time of committing the assault and battery. The only three recent appellate cases found in which a patient was sued by the nurse for assault and battery arose when the patient was an inmate of a mental institution. A California court in 1959 held that a mentally disordered person is civilly responsible for injuries caused by assault and battery.[1] In this particular case a special duty nurse was attending an inmate who was suffering from alcoholism. The nurse was injured in an attempt to restrain the patient from leaving, and sued the patient for assault and battery. The court held that the nurse was not guilty of contributory negligence, and also that she did not assume the risk. The nurse was held entitled to recover under a statute that provided that "A person of unsound mind, of whatever degree, is civilly liable for a wrong done by him."

This does not mean that the nurse need not exercise reasonable care for her own protection in dealing with an insane patient; she is not free to take unreasonable risks. A recent decision of a Hawaii court makes this point clear, saying that "a private duty nurse assumes the risk of injury by an insane patient if by the exercise of due care she could have prevented the injury, or if the hazard was one which it was not reasonable for her to accept in the performance of her duty as a nurse."[2] The Hawaii decision gives the nurse good rules to follow in treating insane patients, from the standpoint of her ability to get redress from the patient in the event of her injury. The basic premise is that the nurse is entitled to recovery from the insane patient for assault and battery. The exceptions are when the nurse fails to exercise that amount of due care for her own safety that would have prevented the injury, and the acceptance of a hazard that it was unreasonable for the nurse to accept in the first place.

Summary

The nurse is generally free to sue a patient when the patient's negligence results in an injury to her, or when the patient commits assault and battery. The nurse is apt to be unsuccessful in her lawsuit for negligence if the negligent act arose during the nurse's performance of her professional functions or could have been avoided by the nurse. However contributory negligence is a valid defense in lawsuits between nurses and patients. When injured by an insane patient the nurse has recourse if she did not have an opportunity to avoid the injury and did not accept an unreasonable hazard.

There are few lawsuits filed against patients by nurses and there is very little opportunity for the nurse to expect success in this kind of lawsuit, especially if the injury occurred within the context of nursing practice. This does not mean that the nurse is completely unprotected in such situations however. The chapter on workmen's compensation discusses the nurse's right to receive a fixed award if she is disabled because of an injury received during the course of her employment.

References

1. Mullen v. Bruce, 335 P. 2d 945 (Calif. 1959); McGuire v. Almy, 8 N.E. 2d 760.
2. Burrows v. Hawaiian Trust Co., 417 P. 2d 816 (Ha. 1966).

10 *Privileged Communications*

The subject of privileged communications is complex and has little relevance to the day to day practice of a registered or practical nurse. The reason for including a chapter on privileged communications at this point is to dispose of the confusion that apparently exists on this subject. The nurse should understand some of the legal responsibilities that exist in this area.

To understand privileged communications, it will be helpful to trace the history of the problem that gave rise to the current law on this subject. The general rule that existed at common law was that a physician could testify in court about any information he gained from his patient during the course of medical practice. If the patient informed the physician that he was guilty of a crime, that he had a venereal disease, that he had a history of mental illness, or revealed anything else of a confidential nature, during a course of a lawsuit the physician could be compelled to reveal this information. In fact at common law the doctor was under legal obligation to do so at the risk of being found in contempt of court. The doctor therefore had no choice, and he testified about matters he would have otherwise treated as confidential.

Knowing that the doctor could be compelled to testify, the patient was faced with the alternatives of either providing the doctor with the secret information and risking the possibility that he might be compelled to testify, or withholding the information from the doctor. Too often the patient chose the latter and withheld information that was vital to the rendering of medical services. It is likely that many patients who chose the alternative of secrecy exaggerated the risk that the doctor would be called upon to testify in court. It is even more likely that the patient believed that the doctor could be compelled to testify about these confidential communications in situations other than the courtroom, which was not so. The public interest was obviously not being served when the

80

patient was being encouraged by a law to withhold information from his attending physician.

Most of the states and provinces resolved this dilemma by enacting privileged communications statutes. These were acts of the state legislatures overriding the common law and providing that under certain circumstances the doctor cannot be compelled to testify about confidential information received from his patients. Privileged communications statutes were later amended in many states and provinces to include communications to the clergy, husband and wife communications, and even communications to accountants. One state extended the privileged communications statute to dentists and three states have extended the statute to nurses.

The privileged communication statutes were enacted for the benefit of the patient. Their purpose is to give the patient some assurance that he will be protected against the doctor or nurse revealing confidential communications, and they are intended to remove the real or imagined fear that the doctor might be compelled to disclose the patient's innermost secrets.

It is a mistake for the nurse to believe that she has become so conversant with the privileged communications statute that she can advise a patient on this matter. The nurse should not point out that there is or is not a privileged communication law in the state in order to entice the patient to reveal information.

Because the privileged communication statute is for the benefit of the patient and not the doctor, the patient is free, if he wishes to do so, to waive this protection, and thus permit the doctor or nurse to testify about such confidential communications. The doctor or nurse who is a witness in a lawsuit does not have any choice with respect to the privileged communication laws. The nurse should answer any questions directed to her when she is serving as a witness, and rely upon the attorneys to object or otherwise resolve the privileged communication problem.

Statutes Directly Applicable to Nurses

Three states have enacted privileged communications statutes that directly provide that some forms of communications to nurses are privileged. The New York Civil Practice Laws and Rules, Section 4504, provide:

> (a) Unless the patient waives the privilege, a person authorized to practice medicine, registered professional nursing, licensed practical nursing or dentistry, shall not be allowed to disclose infor-

mation which he acquired in attending a patient in a professional capacity, and which was necessary to enable him to act in that capacity.

(b) A . . . nurse shall be required to disclose information indicating that a patient who is under the age of 16 years has been the victim of a crime.

(c) A physician or nurse shall be required to disclose any information as to the mental or physical condition of a deceased patient privileged under subdivision (a), except information which will tend to disgrace the memory of the decedent.

Since the privileged communication statute is contrary to common law, the statute is interpreted strictly. Communications are not privileged except when the privilege is specifically granted, and under the circumstances for which it was granted. It should be noted that the New York law does not apply to all confidential information received by the nurse. It only applies to information received "in attending a patient."

Note also that the New York law has two exceptions to the privileged communications statute, when a child is the victim of a crime and when the nurse testifies about the mental or physical condition of a deceased person. The first exception is obviously a result of the overriding public interest in having adequate reports of criminal and other injuries to children. This is reflected in the recent enactments of child abuse laws in many states. The exception for testimony about the physical and mental conditions of a deceased person is the product of the public interest in determining whether an individual was mentally competent at the time he made his will. In both instances the public interest in having the information freely available seemed to the New York legislature to be more important than the encouragement of a patient to make complete disclosures to his nurse or doctor.

In Arkansas the privileged communications statute was amended in 1899 to add nurses,[1] and provides:

> Hereafter no persons authorized to practice physic or surgery and no trained nurses shall be compelled to disclose any information which he may have acquired from his patient while attending in a professional character and which information was necessary to enable him to prescribe as a physician or do any act for him as a trained nurse, provided if two (2) or more physicians or nurses are, or have been in attendance on the patient for the same ailment, the patient by waiving the privilege attaching to any of said physicians or nurses, by calling said physician or nurse to testify concerning said ailment, shall be deemed to have waived the privilege attaching to the other physicians or nurses.

The most recent privileged communications statute which provides expressly for communications made to a nurse is the New Mexico law,[2] which provides:

> A person duly authorized to practice physic or surgery, or a professional or registered nurse, cannot be examined without the consent of his patient as to any communications made by his patient with knowledge to any real or supposed venereal or loathsome disease or any knowledge concerning such disease obtained by personal examination of such patient; nor shall any doctor or nurse employed by a workmen's compensation claimant be examined relating to a workmen's compensation claim without the consent of his patient as to any communication made by his patient with reference to any physical or supposed physical disease or injury or any knowledge obtained by personal examination of such patient except in instances where the doctor has examined or treated the patient at the expense of the employer and such payment is consented to by the patient.

The New Mexico statute obviously reflects some litigation or some other experience under the workmen's compensation laws of that state.

Physician's Privileged Communications Statutes and the Nurse

Because there are only three states that apply the privileged communications statute to nurses, a more important question is whether or not the nurse comes under the physician's privileged communication statute. There are two schools of thought on this subject and the cases and states are split. Some state courts have stated that communications to a nurse are covered by the physician's statute because this is the only way to give full impact to the statute for physicians. Other state courts have taken the position that the privilege is granted only by statute, and unless the statute specifically provides for communications to the nurse, she is not covered. A Nebraska court[3] in 1924 held that the nurse acts as an agent of the physician and stands in the same relationship of confidence to the patient, and therefore should not be permitted to testify for the same reason that the physician is not permitted to testify. A North Dakota court reached the same decision.[4] The Supreme Court of Minnesota[5] said that the physician's privileged communications statute applied when the nurse was acting as an agent or an employee of a physician. The courts of Mississippi,[6] Oklahoma,[7] and Pennsylvania[8] reached the same conclusion. The Pennsylvania court said for the privileged communication statute to apply to communications to a nurse, "the nurse must be acting as an assistant or agent of the doctor and not as an independent person."

When the nurse is acting independently, such as a private duty nurse or a student nurse who prepares a patient's bed in a hospital, communications do not come within the statute.[9] On the other hand, an Arizona court[10] refused to apply the privileged communication statute to a nurse when the law said "physician and patient." The court said if this is to be done, it should be done by the legislature and not the court. An Indiana court[11] said that the privilege does not extend to third persons who were present and overheard conversation unless the third person was necessary for transmitting the information to the physician. A California decision[12] was similar to the decision rendered in Indiana. The Wisconsin courts[13] apparently agreed with the Arizona court as did the courts in Ohio.[14]

Even those states that do apply the physician's privileged communications statutes to nurses do not apply the statutes in all instances. The courts preserve the reason for the statute, which is to encourage the patient to make full disclosure, so that the statute applies only when the patient is giving the physician or nurse confidential information for the purpose of securing health services. A recent decision of an Iowa court[15] clarified this even further when it said that the physician's privileged communication statute applies only when the nurse is acting as an agent or assistant to the physician in charge. The following court decisions illustrate this point.

A New York court[16] held that a nurse could testify that the patient was mentally alert, memory was good, appeared to be interested in life, and in statistics about his farm and produce. The court said this was not a privileged communication since it was not a communication to enable her to act in her professional capacity. Another New York court[17] said that if the facts are such that a layman could have testified, the privileged communications law does not apply. The court added that the privilege did not apply to matters of description relating to or concerning the physical surroundings of the patient, or to communications between the patient and a third person. An Arkansas court[18] said that the privilege did not apply to discussions between the patient's father and the physician about the father's agreement to pay medical expenses. It is very likely that more states will amend their laws to provide for privileged communications made to nurses.

References

1. Arkansas Statutes Annotated, Title 28, Section 607.
2. New Mexico Statutes, Chapter 20, Article 1, Section 20-1-12(d).
3. Culver v. Union P. R. Co., 199 N.W. 794 (Neb. 1924).

4. Meyer v. Russell, 214 N.W. 857 (N. D. 1926).

5. Ostrowski v. Mockridge, 65 N.W. 2d 185 (Minn. 1954).

6. Power & Light Co. v. Jordan, 143 So. 483 (Miss. 1932).

7. Williams v. State, 86 P. 2d 1015 (Okl. 1939); Jasper v. State, 269 P. 2d 375 (Okl. 1954).

8. Gilham v. Gilham, 110 A. 2d 915 (Pa. 1955).

9. Life & Casualty Insurance Co. v. Walters, 177 So. 47 (Miss. 1938).

10. Southwest Metals Co. v. Gomez, 4 F. 2d 215 (Ariz. 1925).

11. General Accident, Fire & Life Assurance Co. v. Tibbs, 2 N.E. 2d 229 (Ind. 1936).

12. Kramer v. Policyholders Life Insurance Assoc., 42 P. 2d 665 (Calif. 1935).

13. Prudential Ins. Co. v. Kozlowski, 276 N.W. 300 (1937).

14. Weis v. Weis, 72 N.E. 2d 245, (Ohio 1947).

15. State v. Tornquist, 120 N.W. 2d 483 (Iowa 1963) (dictum).

16. Re Avery's Estate, 76 N.Y.S. 2d 790 (1948).

17. Re Schermerhorn, 98 N.Y.S. 2d 361 (1950).

18. Cleveland v. Maddox, 239 S.W. 370 (Ark. 1922).

11 *Good Samaritan Legislation*

Since 1961 more than forty states have enacted Good Samaritan legislation, the purpose of which is two-fold: to encourage the practitioner of the healing arts to render roadside emergency care, and to protect the provider of care from later claims of malpractice. Ostensibly the following sequence of events was an everyday occurrence. The kind doctor or other health practitioner would stop at a roadside accident. He would render emergency care using emergency procedures. The patient or his heirs would then sue the doctor for his actions.

Lest the doctor be prone to avoid the next malpractice lawsuit by speeding up when he approaches a roadside accident, the legislatures decided that it is in the public interest to protect the doctor against this kind of lawsuit. Medical and dental societies throughout the nation engaged in a long campaign to get Good Samaritan legislation enacted. The first state to do so was California in 1961, with forty other states following its lead within the next five years. In one state the governor vetoed the bill after the health professions were unable to meet his challenge and produce a documented case of a doctor being subjected to legal harassment for his act of mercy, and soon thereafter the impetus for Good Samaritan legislation died.

The Good Samaritan laws generally provide protection for all practitioners of the healing acts, although some are specifically limited to physicians. Others are limited to physicians and dentists. It is generally agreed that when the law refers to all practitioners of the healing arts, the protection of the law applies to nurses.

The most common provision in the Good Samaritan statute states that the provider of the health services shall be immune to any civil liability for rendering emergency care unless his actions constituted gross negligence or extreme or aggravated malpractice. These terms are usually defined as malpractice and negligence, and they add very little to the law since the provider of services is not liable for resulting injuries unless he is in fact guilty of malpractice or negligence. In essence, the Good Samaritan law says the provider of emergency services cannot be successfully sued unless he was negligent; but the general law of malpractice provides the same test for liability.

The fear that seemed to produce the impetus for Good Samaritan legislation was apparently based on the fact that the individual who renders services under an emergency situation does not have the facilities needed to provide a high level of medical care. But this misses the essential point that the test of malpractice is what the reasonable man would have done "under the same or similar circumstances," the circumstances being that there was a need for services at the roadside and not in the spotless and well-supplied operating room. The very facts of the emergency are the circumstances by which the provider of services will be judged.

Patients have never shown any real tendency to sue the providers of Good Samaritan services, as evidenced by the absence of any appellate decisions on this subject. The doctor would have little problem winning the sympathy of a jury if he were sued for rendering emergency care. The nurse who is called upon, perhaps by her conscience, to render roadside medical care has the same legal protection whether or not a Good Samaritan statute exists in her state or province. If she acts at a level of care not below that of the reasonably prudent nurse under the same or similar circumstances, she is undoubtedly not liable.

If the nurse witnesses an accident or injuries that require immediate medical attention, she should not attempt to control the situation unless she first determines that there is a true emergency which requires immediate treatment, and she is the individual who is best qualified and willing to render emergency treatment. If she undertakes medical care in such a fashion as to constitute the practice of medicine, she is not engaged in the unlicensed practice of medicine if a true emergency situation exists. The requirements for medical licensure usually state an exemption in the emergency situation. The nurse faced with a true emergency should do only what is necessary to preserve life and what the emergency dictates, and she should turn the patient over to a physician for continued treatment as soon as possible. Perhaps the one risk that the nurse takes when she engages in medical practice in the emergency situation is that there might not have been an emergency after all. But here the question will not be whether the emergency existed, but whether the reasonably prudent nurse would have been convinced that the emergency existed and acted accordingly.

The nurse should not undertake to perform independent medical services when a physician is available. If a physician later comes on the scene the nurse should turn the patient over to the physician and indicate what services she has rendered to this point.

If the patient does file suit against the nurse then the only relevant question is whether the patient suffered an injury arising out of the nurse's failure to act in a reasonable manner under the circumstances. It is doubtful that any nurse would lose a lawsuit based on this sequence of events, unless she acted in a manner totally detrimental to the patient's welfare.

Sometimes the question arises whether or not the nurse or doctor rendering emergency services has a legal duty to continue those services after the patient has been placed in an ambulance or taken to a hospital. Again the test is reasonableness. There is nothing that the law says that specifically requires that the nurse or doctor continue treatment once the patient has been placed in a hospital, or in the hands of other competent medical practitioners.

The nurse may not always be able to decide whether or not to render emergency treatment that is obviously medical practice. The nurse may not possess the usual competency of the physician or surgeon, but in their absence she may be the most qualified individual to act. In that case it would seem that her moral responsibilities would override any legal considerations and compel her to render emergency treatment.

Good Samaritan legislation has been opposed by some well meaning legislators who see it as an attempt on the part of the health professions to place themselves above the law and make themselves immune from lawsuits for their actions. Because the Good Samaritan statutes are generally meaningless, the arguments against them are equally meaningless. It undoubtedly behooves the health professions not to pursue these statutes when there is even token resistance in the state legislature.

12   *The Nurse in the Intensive Care Unit*

When the nurse fulfills her typical role in an intensive care unit there is theoretically no difference in her legal responsibilities than when she practices in a medical office or a more typical hospital situation. Practically speaking, some unusual and significant legal problems may arise in her obligations under the nursing practice acts and her responsibilities to her patients.

Nursing Practice Acts

The nursing practice acts are perhaps the most liberal of all professional licensing laws for auxiliary health personnel. Most of them permit the nurse to do almost anything in the medical area that is prescribed by the doctor or done under his direction and control. In general the restrictions that are imposed upon other auxiliaries in the health professions are not imposed upon the nurse. However this liberal control over the nurse has not resulted in a large number of charges that the nurse has expanded her functions into the area of general medical practice, or that physicians have been derelict by delegating functions that are beyond the education and training of the nurse, since in most instances the nurse is acting within the limitations of the nursing practice act if her activities are limited by direction, control, and supervision. When the nurse strays into the independent practice of medicine without benefit of these controls, she undoubtedly violates the medical practice act of her state.

When the nurse is assigned to an intensive care unit in a hospital there is a serious possibility that she may be called upon to provide nonemergency medical functions that lie within the legal definition of the practice of medicine and are not protected by the definition of the practice of nursing. The medical profession is not unaware of the fact that there may be a substantial legal problem when the intensive care unit nurse performs the medical functions expected in this assignment.[1] If the nurse is in fact violating the state medical law, she is guilty of a crime; if the doctor and hospital instruct her to violate the law by training her and placing her in this capacity, they are participating in a conspiracy to violate the law.

If the purpose of the intensive care unit is correctly understood, it is to provide medical services as quickly as possible when time is a critical factor. Medical experts will agree that the nurse is the most important factor in the intensive care unit, since she is often the first person on the scene and must give emergency treatment. Here the problem arises. What is the nurse's responsibility under the law when she is the first to reach the patient and there is need for immediate action?

In a study of the *Legal Aspects of Public Health Service Medical Care*, published by the United States Department of Health, Education and Welfare, it is stated (page 53) that:

> All nurses, and particularly those assigned to intensive care units or recovery rooms should be familiar with closed chest cardio-pulmonary resuscitation techniques, since these people will generally be in a position to institute prompt life saving measures.

When the cardiac monitor alarm goes off in an intensive care unit, one nurse immediately takes the pulse and blood pressure, and if they are faint she starts external cardiac massage, establishes an airway, or uses mouth to mouth resuscitation while another nurse goes for a physician. Nurses may even be trained with elective cardioversions and do successful defibrillations.[2] It is clear that the nurse's functions here are being increased far beyond that permitted by most nursing practice acts, and that she performs these functions without the direction and control of a physician. When the nurse arrives on the scene she acts according to her training and general directions, but she is nevertheless exercising professional medical judgment and professional medical skills, thereby violating the medical practice acts.

It could be argued that these are emergency situations and the law commonly disregards the need for medical licensure in such a situation. This argument probably would not be accepted by the courts, however, because this is not a true emergency situation but a planned one. It is known that emergencies will arise in the intensive care unit, and the nurse is specifically placed there to provide medical skills until a physician is available. It is very likely that the sole reason for the nurse being in this position, rather than a physician, is that there are not sufficient numbers of physicians available to fill these assignments. This creates the presumption that the doctors, hospitals, and nurses are conspiring to violate the medical practice acts by assigning the nurse to act as a physician.

It is generally realized that some of the medical acts are being violated here. Whether or not this really presents a practical problem is another matter. Good sense would seem to dictate that if the role of the nurse should be expanded in the intensive care units for the benefit of the public, the nursing and medical acts should not stand in the way. This may mean continuing to violate the medical laws while a concerted effort is being made to review the laws and amend them if necessary, which must be done in each jurisdiction because the definitions in the medical and nursing laws vary substantially from one state to the next. It should be incumbent upon the medical and nursing professions in each state to ask the state legislature to amend the definitions if necessary, in order to remove the doctors, hospitals, and nurses from apparent jeopardy.

Claims that nurses are engaged in the unlicensed practice of medicine are relatively uncommon. This may stem from the fact that in most instances no one is in a position to complain. Certainly the doctors, hospitals, and nursing supervisors participating in assigning these functions would not complain. Complaint could, however, come from another physician who opposes the delegation of functions, a patient (or his heirs) who raises the issue in a malpractice lawsuit, or a random investigation by the state agency charged with enforcing medical and nursing laws. When one balances the technical violation of the law with the public interest in maintaining and operating effective intensive care units the conclusion seems obvious.

There is a report in the literature of an intensive care unit that is operating in Michigan without physicians.[3] Here specially trained nurses administer emergency care to cardiac attack patients. Before the unit was opened the nurses were taught basic electrocardiography, cardiac function and anatomy, and symptoms and treatment of heart disease. The nurses were taught to do actual elective heart work. The nurses in this unit are given the right (by the hospital) to bypass the emergency room with every cardiac suspect who enters the hospital. According to this report the Michigan Heart Association passed a resolution in recognition of the hospital's success, "approving the use of defibrillators on patients by properly trained nurses when the patient requires such treatment and in the absence of a physician."

The medicolegal problem exists in spite of the success of the unit, although it is not suggested that the medicolegal problem takes precedence over the public interest in maintaining this unit. The fact is that the hospital and the Michigan Heart Association have no authority to amend the laws of the state. If the acts performed by the nurses are in violation of these laws, approval by the hospital and the heart association do not mitigate the violation. Obviously the solution is to amend the law if the acts are prohibited by it.

Malpractice

When the nurse undertakes a responsibility for which she is not normally suited by training, she naturally takes the risk of increasing the chances of malpractice claims. However no cases have been found in which malpractice claims have been brought against nurses and physicians working in intensive care units. This may be due to a number of intangibles that are subject to speculation. It could be that the patients and their families fully appreciate the outstanding services which are provided in these situations, or it could be that the chances of successful lawsuits are so remote that no one bothers to sue. The fact that the patient has been assigned to an intensive care unit in itself indicates that the patient was in such a condition that death was not unexpected. In these cases it would be difficult to prove that the patient's death was a result of the nurse's negligence rather than natural causes.

The legal question for the nurse is whether or not she is negligent in presuming to perform certain functions without being licensed as a physician, and more important, whether or not the hospital is negligent in assigning someone other than a licensed physician to take this responsibility.

When a nurse is assigned to an intensive care unit she agrees to perform a level of services that she undoubtedly did not anticipate when she entered nursing training. There are few other situations where there is as much strain and reliance placed on the nurse, since there is an unusually high level of performance expected of her in this situation. It is only conjecture at this point, but it is conceivable that a court considering the question may find that the nurse accepting this assignment that is beyond her normal capacities, acted in a negligent manner in agreeing to the assignment. Hopefully when the courts are called upon to consider the situation they will be impressed with its redeeming quality, the ability of the units to prolong and maintain human lives.

Because of the nature of the intensive care unit the nurse is exposed to more deaths than she normally would be in general nursing practice. One might conclude that this could mean an increased number of lawsuits. However the fact that intensive care units have been operating for a number of years without reported lawsuits indicates that the exposure to lawsuits is less than average when working in a unit of this kind.

There are other factors that tend to indicate that this type of practice places the nurse in greater danger of lawsuits than the average nurse. When the hospital has only a few nurses specially trained to do this work, it may impose too great a mental and physical burden on them, and in any situation when doctors and nurses lose their proper perspective relative to the patient there are likely to be more injuries and legal claims. It is clear that the nurse's best protection against malpractice claims in the intensive care unit are her training and ability to react in an emergency situation, and her own mental attitude toward her patients.

Other Dangers

There are two other dangers in the intensive care unit that warrant comment. First, there is a propensity for spreading infection in the intensive care unit. The nurse should be aware of this problem and attuned to the fact that extreme care is necessary in these units to avoid the spread of infectious diseases. If she has an infectious disease she should report this to her supervisor in all instances, but particularly if she is working in an intensive care unit. Second, the large number of electrical devices used in the intensive care unit present some hazard. Many of these devices were probably not meant to be used in close proximity to so many other electronic devices. Leakage from electrical equipment and devices is a threat to patients who have low resistance pathways to the heart.

Summary

There have been no malpractice suits reported against nurses in intensive care units, even though the nature of this work would suggest that the nurse would have a greater exposure to lawsuits than in other types of nursing practice.

The nurse who works in the intensive care unit is potentially being called upon to practice medicine without a license. The exception to the licensure rule in the case of an emergency probably would not be upheld by the courts, since the hospital, physicians, and nurses involved appreciate the fact that when the nurse is assigned to this responsibility she is called upon to render medical treatment. It is strongly recommended that the practice acts be amended, that only qualified nurses be assigned to intensive care units, and that there be some legal protection (insurance) provided by the hospital. Extensive training for the nurse is perhaps the most important part of her protection against lawsuits in this environment.

References

1. More authority sought for coronary care nurse. *Journal of the American Hospital Association,* July 16, 1966, page 118.

2. For a recent report on coronary care units, especially with regard to the role of the nurse, see the *Journal of the American Medical Association,* July 31, 1967, p. 28.

3. Small Michigan hospital lauded for nurse-operated coronary unit. *Modern Hospital,* December 1966, p. 28.

13   *Industrial Nursing*

Although this chapter has been titled *Industrial Nursing*, the more current terminology is "occupational health nursing." The term "industrial nurse" is undoubtedly more widely used, but because the nurse performs health services in commercial and service enterprises other than industry, the term "occupational health nurse" would seem to be more appropriate. Appended to this book is a publication prepared by the American Medical Association's Council on Occupational Health, titled "Guide for Development of Medical Directives for Occupational Health Nurses," which describes procedures to be used by occupational health nurses.

Malpractice

Under the law there is no significant difference between the obligations of the occupational health nurse and those of the nurse who practices in the more conventional hospital or medical office location. The same general principles of malpractice apply to the nurse working in a commercial enterprise in that she is personally liable for her negligent actions and has the same duty of care toward her patients as do other nurses.

In the hospital and medical office context, the injured patient can usually sue the nurse's employer for her negligent acts. This may not necessarily be true when the nurse is employed by a commercial, industrial, or service enterprise because there may be some additional factors present. The nurse's employer is the corporation or business enterprise and would be expected to be subject to liability for the nurse's actions under the principle of *respondeat superior*, since this principle is not reserved for the malpractice situation alone and has general application to all employer-employee situations when the employee is acting in furtherance of the employment relation.

The complicating factor is that the employer may not be subject to a lawsuit brought by one of his employees, and it is likely that the patients of the industrial nurse would be the employees of the same person or business that employs the nurse. The application of the workmen's compensation law may thus operate to protect the employer from a lawsuit based upon the negligent conduct of the industrial nurse and *respondeat superior*. The protection that the employer receives by virtue of the workmen's compensation law works against the industrial nurse, because the injured employee has one less person to sue and he is more apt to sue the nurse.

There is another factor that has not yet been mentioned. In many states the law protects one employee against lawsuits for negligent acts brought by other employees when the negligent acts were committed during the course of employment. This would seem to say that the industrial nurse cannot be sued by a fellow employee. Since law is very uncertain in this area, it is suggested that the nurse not unduly rely on this kind of legal protection. The nurse working in occupational health should be particularly sensitive to the need for adequate malpractice insurance coverage and she should make sure that the policy provides coverage in this context.

Nurses employed in occupational or industrial nursing seem to have been sued a disproportionate number of times for malpractice. This is not surprising since the injured party may have only one person to sue, the nurse, in contrast to the medical office or hospital situation where there are other available defendants. The other relevant factor is that the industrial nurse is not working under the direct supervision and control of a physician and thus does not have ready access to his opinion and consultation. It is not a reflection on professional nurses who engage in industrial or occupational health nursing to point out there is an increased exposure to malpractice claims, because this is obviously a result of the nature of their practice.

The one area of malpractice claims that presents a unique problem for the nurse is the decision whether or not to refer the patient to the physician. The industrial nurse is called upon to make this decision more often than most other nurses. The nursing practice acts, read together with the medical practice acts, do not permit the nurse to engage in medical diagnosis. This may be the rule of thumb for the nurse to use. If the injury or other ailment appears to require a diagnosis, the nurse should not treat the patient herself except for emergency care. If the nurse makes a diagnosis she is engaged in the unlicensed practice of medicine and she will be found guilty of malpractice if any injury to the patient results. This begs the question (unanswerable) of whether the nurse can ever treat a patient without making a diagnosis of some kind.

In this situation the nurse should not hesitate to refer patients to physicians or indicate a need for further medical treatment. The industrial nurse must condition herself to resist the temptation to treat the patient herself when she really knows that the patient is in need of medical care. The malpractice actions brought against industrial nurses are usually based on the failure of the nurse to refer the patient to a physician or the failure to diagnose a serious problem and the continued treatment of the case as if it were a simple matter of indigestion or other minor ailment.

Nursing Practice Acts

Although the industrial nurse is specifically mentioned in only some of the nursing practice acts, the fact that she is engaged in this form of nursing practice does not give her any greater latitude to engage in medical practice than other nurses. The employer of the industrial nurse has no legal authority to compel the nurse to engage in medical practice, nor does the permission or even the direction of the employer for the nurse to engage in medical practice have any relevance if the nurse is so charged, and the nurse should be especially wary when the employer seems to be concerned with having the industrial nurse engage in the unlicensed practice of medicine.

The industrial nurse who works under the indirect supervision of a physician must realize that even the physician does not have the legal authority to authorize her to engage in medical practice. Many of the procedures that she could legally perform if the physician were present are prohibited if she is not working under his direction and control. The nurse must ignore any standing order given her by some absentee physician that purports to authorize her to engage in medical practice. She would be foolish in relying upon this order since the doctor does not have the authority to increase her statutory authority. The nurse who makes the mistake of relying on one of these improper standing orders risks the criminal charge of engaging in the unlicensed practice of medicine and the revocation of her nursing license. The only acceptable standing orders are those that outline the nurse's duties and functions, perhaps giving some basic rules of first aid, and they do not increase her functions to the point of medical practice. The appended guide should be the basis for the industrial nurse's standing orders.

Because of the difficult decisions and responsibilities of a legal, health, and moral nature placed on the industrial nurse it has been recommended that nurses not engage in this form of nursing practice until they have obtained some experience in clinics, out-patient hospitals, or similar situations where they have treated, under a doctor's supervision, the kinds of problems that can be expected to arise in the occupational health situations. Although no court cases have been found on this point it is conceivable that a court might find that the nurse acts in an unreasonable manner and is guilty of malpractice when she accepts a position as an industrial nurse without being qualified for such a position by experience.

14   *The Expert Witness*

The nurse, like other citizens, is subject to being called into court to testify as a witness. She may be called because she has witnessed a crime, an automobile accident, or a similar event that ends in a courtroom test of the facts. In such cases she relates her account of the event without necessarily relying on the skills and abilities peculiar to her profession. A nurse who is asked to testify as an "eyewitness" should consider this imposition on her time as a civic duty. When the nurse is called on to testify in court because of her specialized knowledge as a nurse, she is called as an "expert witness."

There are three general situations in which a nurse may be called on to testify in court because she is a nurse. Most obvious is the situation in which she is sued for malpractice and testifies on her own behalf as a defendant, according to her recollection of the facts that are the basis for the lawsuit. Second, in a lawsuit involving the contest of a will the nurse may be called upon to testify about the mental capacities of the patient at the time he made the will. She may be called by the party testing the will or by the party defending the will. In either case the nurse will be testifying as to her own observations and conclusions. Third, the nurse may be called to testify in a lawsuit against another nurse. This chapter will deal with the rights, responsibilities, and experiences of a nurse called on by the defendant or the plaintiff to testify as an expert witness in a malpractice lawsuit against another nurse.

The Use of Expert Witnesses

Expert witnesses are used in many different kinds of lawsuits. To warrant the use of an expert witness in a lawsuit, two elements must be present: The subject of the inference must be so directly related to some science, profession, business, or occupation as to be beyond the general understanding of the average layman; and the witness must have some skill, knowledge, or experience in that field, so that his opinion or inference will be an aid in discovering the truth. Thus before a person may testify as an expert witness he must show his qualifications. Practical experience as well as academic learning may qualify an individual as an expert.

As discussed in Chapter 4, the decision whether a nurse is guilty of malpractice usually depends on whether she has lived up to the standard of care of the reasonably prudent nurse. The "prudent man" rule requires that the nurse act in the same manner as the reasonably prudent nurse in the locale would have acted in the same or similar circumstances.

We recall that it is up to the plaintiff to prove that the nurse was negligent in not living up to the standard of care. In order to prove his case the plaintiff must demonstrate to the court what he believes the reasonably prudent nurse would have done under the same or similar circumstances and must show that this was not how the treatment was rendered by the nurse whom he is suing. He must also prove the standard of care of the locale. To do this, he must secure one or more nurses who are qualified as experts to testify concerning the standards of care. The defendant nurse may then call on her own expert witnesses to testify as to what they believe to be the standard of care. It is to be expected that the witness called by the plaintiff will suggest that the defendant acted in a manner below the standard of care and that the defendant's expert witnesses will testify that the defendant met the standard of care and acted as the reasonably prudent nurse would have acted under the same or similar circumstances. The defendant nurse is legally obliged to demonstrate only that she acted in a reasonable manner and is therefore not liable for malpractice, even though she did not live up to the standard of care of the best nurse. The conflicting expert witnesses will testify, and the court or jury will make the final judgment of whether or not the defendant acted according to the standard of care of the reasonably prudent nurse.

Who May Be Called as an Expert Witness?

Although any registered nurse may be called on to testify as an expert witness, usually the one called upon will not be familiar with the patient or the nurse being sued. An expert witness is called because of her general knowledge of nursing and not because of her familiarity with the particular case. In a malpractice case, the nurses most likely to be called are those with faculty appointments, those acting in supervisory capacities, or those who are authors of textbooks. The reason for selecting such individuals is obvious; the attorney choosing the expert witness wants to create the impression that his expert is more learned than the expert selected by the other side. However, this does not always work, as in one case in which it was shown that a well-known expert in his field had not seen a patient in ten years.

There are other important considerations in selecting an expert witness. Because the law usually refers to the standard of care in the locale, the expert selected is usually from the same general area as the nurse being sued. Also, the nurse must truly be an expert in the area under consideration.

Attorneys who engage in many malpractice lawsuits know the experts who are available and are continually requested to testify in malpractice cases. An expert witness loses some of his value when it can be shown in court that he has consistently taken either the defendant's or the plaintiff's point of view while testifying in a large number of malpractice cases.

Therefore, in selecting an expert the attorney and his client will look for a nurse who is highly qualified in her field, is able to convey an impression of sincerity and reliability, is well-known in the community, has no long history of testifying in malpractice lawsuits, and most important, believes that the nurse in question did or did not act according to the standard of care.

A nurse asked to testify as an expert witness is under no legal compulsion to do so, and may refuse without penalty. It is only when the nurse has seen the patient for the purpose of rendering professional care that she is subject to subpoena.

The Expert Witness Is not an Advocate

Although she testifies for one side of a case, the expert witness is not an advocate for that side in the sense that the attorney is an advocate. She is being paid for her expert opinion and should give it openly and honestly at all times. The expert may be considered to be an advocate only with respect to refraining from voluntarily offering information that will be beneficial to the other side. Under some circumstances, it could be argued that here, too, the expert witness has an obligation to speak. An expert should not lie or otherwise color her judgment, even if the true answer would be prejudicial to the side for which she is testifying.

Some expert witnesses mistakenly believe that their position as an expert requires that they try the case as an advocate. This is unwise for a number of reasons, the major one being that the expert witness is a nurse and not an attorney, and trying cases does not come within the area of her expertise. It is foolhardy for the expert witness to advocate the case from the witness stand, and the expert who ventures to do so may put the client's case in jeopardy. The jury may distrust the witness who seems to be overly concerned with the outcome of the case. The expert witness who attempts to advocate the case has no complaint when the opposing attorney treats her as an advocate.

Testimony of the Expert Witness

When the expert witness testifies, the attorney for the side calling him as a witness will elicit his testimony by asking simple questions that give the expert an opportunity to give his evaluation of the case. On cross-examination, the other attorney will probably do his best to discredit the testimony, create confusion, and in other ways make it appear that this witness is not an expert.

The "have you stopped beating your wife" question is very apt to arise during cross-examination. The expert's response to this type of question depends greatly on the laws of the state in which the trial is held. In some states an expert witness must answer "yes" or "no" to all questions; in others he is free to state that he cannot give a "yes" or "no" answer to the question; and in still others he must first answer "yes" or "no" and may then ask the judge for permission to explain his answer. The expert witness must rely on the attorney for the side that called him to protect him in this situation. A nurse asked to testify as an expert should ask the attorney what the rule is in her state concerning this. When she is forced to answer "yes" or "no," she may get a chance to explain her answer when she is again examined by the first attorney, who will ask her if she wishes to explain her earlier answer.

The Expert Witness and the Lawyer

Under our system of law the two contending attorneys present their clients' points of view as advocates. Each is not acting as an independent investigator attempting to discover the truth, but rather as an advocate of one point of view. This method of determining the truth, which is well established in Anglo-Saxon legal systems, may seem repugnant to the nurse and the scientist who are accustomed to working either as individuals or in a group to obtain the facts.

Our legal system is something of a throwback to ancient England where knights on horseback jousted to the death to determine whose patron was right in a controversy. Each of the competing parties hired as his champion the man whom he considered to be the best jouster, and the dispute was settled by the battle of the champions.

The attorney today is his client's champion and he jousts with the opposing attorney. The attorney tries to find the best possible expert witness and through direct examination make him appear in the most favorable light. He tries to discredit the testimony of the opponent's expert witness whenever possible on cross-examination. In cross-examination of the expert witness, animosity may develop between the expert and the attorney if the expert takes the attorney's cross-examination as a personal affront. The nurse testifying as an expert witness should not permit herself to become emotionally involved in the lawsuit. She should not resent cross-examination, nor should she fear it. If an attorney exceeds the bounds of propriety in his cross-examination, the expert witness can rely on the attorney for the other side to object and cause the line of questioning to be redirected. Some of the suggestions contained later in this chapter may help the nurse to understand and appreciate cross-examination and endure it with no lasting effect.

Compensation for the Expert Witness

A nurse who testifies as an expert witness is entitled to compensation for her service, and she should not hesitate to request a fee commensurate with the time and effort that will go into her preparation for and participation in the case. A minimum compensation for the expert witness is sometimes set by state statute, but this does not prohibit or in any way make unethical the acceptance of a considerably larger fee. Under no circumstances should the nurse accept compensation for her services on a contingent fee basis, because this gives her a vested interest in the outcome of the case that could either color or appear to color her testimony. A nurse will first be asked to evaluate the case and to indicate to the attorney whether the nurse being sued acted according to the standard of care required of the reasonably prudent nurse. After the nurse has indicated her viewpoint on the case, she may or may not be asked to testify as an expert witness. Thus the nurse will have no vested interest in the outcome.

If a nurse is asked on cross-examination whether or not she is receiving a fee, she should not hesitate to answer in the affirmative, since paying a fee to an expert witness is accepted practice and the judge, attorney, and probably the jury already know that she is receiving a fee. Accepting a fee does not mean that the nurse is giving a false evaluation of the case.

In many instances, the attorney giving his final address to the jury, or even the judge charging the jury, will state that there is nothing to indicate that a nurse who receives a fee as an expert witness is unreliable, and will advise the jury not to consider this fee in their deliberations.

Suggestions for the Expert Witness

Don't agree to testify unless you believe in the point of view you are called on to support.

Don't hesitate to admit on the witness stand that you have conferred with the attorney prior to the trial. How else would you have been called to testify?

Don't voluntarily state that you have not been coached to give a particular opinion. You are not on trial and don't have to defend yourself.

Don't try the case from the witness stand. Don't try to be an advocate.

Speak in language that will be readily understood by a layman. Use the popular names for anatomy.

Answer the questions as asked and refrain from answering unasked questions.

Don't exaggerate or attempt to overstate your conclusions.

Don't hestitate to say "I do not know" or otherwise admit that you cannot answer a particular question.

If you cannot answer a question with a "yes" or "no" answer, say so. Let the judge decide whether the question must be answered.

Don't anticipate questions. Wait for the specific question and answer it.

Pause briefly before all your answers, especially when the question has been asked by the other attorney. This gives your attorney the opportunity to object if necessary and also gives the jury a better impression of your answer.

If you believe that the other expert witnesses are wrong or that other authorities are wrong don't hestitate to disagree with their ideas. Direct your disagreement at the ideas and not at the individuals.

Don't be belligerent towards the attorney for the other side or act in any way that might give the impression that he is your opponent.

Don't argue the law with either attorney.

Don't lose your temper or exhibit any anger toward the other attorney. This may be exactly what he wants.

Don't be smug, conveying the impression that only nurses know anything about nursing, since this will often alienate the jury. A modest attitude is preferable.

Do accept a fee for your services, commensurate with the time and effort you spend on the case.

Don't agree to testify on a contingent basis; i.e., don't make any agreement by which you will get a fee or a larger fee if your side wins the case.

Don't hestitate to admit on the witness stand that you are being paid for your services as an expert witness.

Alternatives to the Expert Witness

A number of attempts have been made to find a substitute for the expert witness system, especially in medical and dental malpractice actions. In some states the courts apply the doctrine of *res ipsa loquitur* (it speaks for itself). This abolishes the need for the testimony of the expert witness, saying that the facts of the case are such that a lay jury can reach its decision without the benefit of expert testimony. It appears that more and more states are willing to apply this doctrine in medical malpractice cases, although some states vehemently refuse to do so. When it is used, it is generally limited to those situations in which the court believes that the facts of the case will be clear to lay people and that the nature of the injury to the patient is one that does not occur without negligence. To some extent, the application of *res ipsa loquitur* presumes to place a burden of guilt upon the defendant and requires him to prove that his conduct was up to the standards of the reasonably prudent doctor.

Res ipsa loquitur is still a fairly new doctrine and there is much more to be learned about it. Sometimes it is stated that the doctrine arose because of the reluctance of doctors to testify against each other, the so-called conspiracy of silence. This charge has never been substantiated and can probably be attributed to the fact that some very doubtful malpractice lawsuits are brought against doctors in which it is impossible to get an expert to testify for the patient because no expert can be found who honestly believes in the plaintiff's case.

Most of the plans for finding substitutes for the expert witness system have been tried on a local or a regional basis through the joint cooperation of medical and bar associations. One system calls for the parties in a malpractice lawsuit to agree to use impartial or independent medical testimony, with the parties to the suit contributing equally to the expert's fee and both sides agreeing that he shall be the sole medical expert. Naturally this agreement is made before either party learns of the decisions of the impartial expert.

In some parts of the country the medical associations have created committees which review claims brought against physicians. These medical review committees recommend whether the claim should be settled out of court or defended. This mechanism is often used where there are group malpractice policies in effect. If the committee believes that the doctor should defend the case they may assist him in getting expert witnesses.

Some medicolegal groups have created panels wherein the doctors assigned to the panel agree to testify in rotation when their turn arises. This system is usually employed in conjunction with some system of prior review to discourage groundless or nuisance claims and to encourage out of court settlements when there is proof of malpractice. Many such programs are being tried, but at the present time there has been no proved substitute for the use of expert witnesses in malpractice lawsuits.

Because of the relatively few malpractice cases brought against nurses there has been little effort to find alternatives to the expert witness in nursing malpractice cases.

15   *Wills*

The nature of her profession requires that the nurse have some basic understanding of the law pertaining to wills. The nurse may be called upon to witness a will, or to testify as to the testator's mental capacity at the time he made his will. There may be problems associated with the nurse being named as a beneficiary in a patient's will. In addition the nurse may be interested in her own will.

Witnessing a Will

A private duty nurse or a hospital nurse may be called upon by a patient to witness a will, which means that she signs a statement at the bottom of the will indicating that she saw the testator sign the will. Sometimes the testator makes a statement that this is his will and he has signed it, and the witness then signs an attestation clause. In any event the important element is that the nurse may be called upon to sign such a clause in the patient's will, which usually requires that the nurse either see the patient sign the will he declares to be his, or attest to the patient's statement that the will is his and he has signed it.

Ideally, the person witnessing a will should be someone substantially younger than the testator, and someone who will be available at the testator's death, since the purpose of having witnesses is to have someone available at a later date to testify that the testator had the necessary mental capacity to make the will and knew what he was signing at that time.

If the nurse is asked by a patient to witness a will she may not be in a position to refuse. Inasmuch as the law requires two or three witnesses and the attorney who drew the will is usually reluctant to sign as a witness, there may not be anyone else available to witness the will. Close personal friends or family members who are apt to be beneficiaries under a will are usually reluctant to be witnesses, since this may create problems if the will is later contested.

If the nurse agrees to witness a will she should see the patient sign. If the patient does not sign the will in the nurse's presence then she should not sign the clause at the end of the will that states that she saw the patient sign. If the patient has already signed outside the nurse's presence she should ask the patient to sign again, or ask the patient if this is his will and if he signed it. If the patient answers in the affirmative to both questions the nurse can sign her name to a simple statement at the end of the will indicating that the testator declared to her that this was his will and that he signed it. A nurse would be very foolish to agree to witness a will after the patient has died, or when the patient is not present.

If the nurse is a minor she should refuse to witness the will. If the nurse is likely to be a beneficiary under the will she should also refuse to witness it. If the nurse is asked by a relative or friend to witness a will that she did not see the testator sign, she should not agree to witness the will, since by signing the will the nurse is indicating that she either saw the testator sign or he said he had signed it, and in her opinion the testator knew exactly what had taken place.

For there to be effective witnessing of a will the witness need not know or be informed about the contents of the will or be told who the beneficiaries will be. All that is required is that she witness it. However there are two kinds of wills that do not need witnesses' signatures, holographic and nuncupative wills.

A *holographic will* is a will completely written, dated, and signed by the testator, and it does not need to be witnessed. In general the state laws have departed from their prior position of accepting holographic wills. Now when holographic wills are permitted by state courts they are limited to unusual situations, such as when it is impossible to get witnesses or when the testator is in the armed forces. Holographic wills are generally not recognized in England but they are specifically permitted in a number of Canadian provinces.

A *nuncupative will* is a verbal will. These are accepted as valid wills, in most jurisdictions with some limitations. The most serious limitation on nuncupative wills found in the statutes limits their validity to disposition of personal property, usually up to a specific dollar amount. This prohibits distributing real estate by a verbal will. The nuncupative will is also limited to situations when the testator is in his last sickness and the will is made in the presence of witnesses. The testator must call upon these witnesses to bear witness that he is making a will. A nuncupative will must also be set down in writing and admitted to probate as soon as possible. The statutes providing for nuncupative wills vary substantially from state to state and it would not be justified to do anything more than suggest to the nurse that she may be called upon to listen to and witness an oral will.

The legal effect of the will, depending so much on the specific language of the statute, must be left to the lawyers to determine.

Special privileges are granted for wills made by soldiers and sailors. A leading court decision involved a member of the Royal Air Force who was killed while training in Canada.[1] The court held in this case that a soldier "in active military service" is privileged to make a will without any formalities. In most states some provision is made for such wills.

Mental Capacity

If the nurse witnesses a will she may be called upon at a later date to testify regarding the mental capacity of the patient to make the will. This will occur if someone contests the will after the patient's death and a hearing is held during probate of the will to determine if it is valid. The nurse who witnessed the will may be called upon to state that she did or did not witness the will, and that she did or did not see the testator sign the will. The nurse will also be asked to testify about the patient's mental state at the time the will was signed. For a will to be effective the testator must have had the necessary mental capacity to make a will. Some courts use the following definition of mental capacity:

> . . . at the time of the execution of the will, had such mind as would enable a person to transact common and simple kinds of business with the intelligence which belongs to the weakest class of sound minds, together with a memory sufficient to recall the general nature, condition and extent of her property and her relations to those to whom she gave and also to those from whom she excluded her bounty.

A person may be incapable of managing and conserving a large estate and yet be perfectly able to understand the nature of a will, to comprehend the extent of his property, and to recall the natural objects of his bounty. A person may require a guardian to supervise his estate and yet be competent enough to make a valid will disposing of it upon his death.

In determining the mental capacity of the testator, great reliance is placed upon the statements and testimony of the persons who witnessed the will. For this reason, when a will is being signed and witnessed the attorney usually engages the testator and witnesses in conversation that will give the witnesses some later basis for stating that the testator possessed the necessary mental capacity at the time the will was signed and witnessed. In addition to the testimony of witnesses, great weight is placed upon the testimony of attending physicians and nurses to establish that the testator had the required mental capacity at the time he executed his will, which means that the physician and the nurse attending the patient may be called upon to testify regarding the patient's mental capacity on the day the will was signed, even though they were not witnesses to the will. The courts have established that a nurse may be called upon to testify as to the mental capacity of the patient.[2] If the nurse is called upon to do this during a probate hearing, she does nothing more than state her observations and impressions. The court or the jury will evaluate her comments and reach its own decision about the mental capacity of the patient at the time he made his will.

The Nurse as a Beneficiary

As a general rule there is no reason why a nurse cannot be a beneficiary under a patient's will. Patients can and do leave portions of their estate to nurses, and these legacies have been upheld by the courts. The problem that sometimes arises is the claim that the patient was under the undue influence of the nurse at the time the will was prepared. There have been series of lawsuits brought to contest wills made by patients who had been nursed by private duty nurses and left substantial portions of their estates to them. The fact that a portion of the estate is left to a nurse does not in itself mean that the nurse has exercised any undue influence over the patient. The burden of proving undue influence rests with the individual who is making this claim and contesting the will.

It is very difficult to establish undue influence. If the nurse hoped to be, asked to be, and was rewarded for her kindness, it does not necessarily follow that she used undue influence on her patient. As one court said, undue influence involves improper means and practices. Influence gained by kindness and affection will not be regarded as undue influence if no imposition of fraud is practiced, even though it induced the testator to make an unequal disposition of his property.

The Nurse's Will

For a nurse to make her own will disposing of her assets upon her death, she must have "testamentary capacity," that is, the mental capacity to make the will, and the necessary age. Statutes usually set the minimum age at which a will may be made and in most cases this age is 21. In most states the age limit is lower for women than for men and in some cases the age limits vary depending on whether or not the testator is disposing of real or personal property. The old rule prohibiting wills by married women has virtually disappeared so that a married woman is now free to make her own will. Some general information on wills may be helpful to the nurse in making her own will.

Intestate Distribution

In the event an individual dies without a will he is said to have died "intestate." When an individual dies intestate the law implies a will, and the law determines the method by which the individual's property is distributed. If an unmarried woman dies leaving children, the law of most states will divide her property equally among the children. If she dies without leaving children the surviving parent or parents share the estate. If the unmarried woman dies without leaving children or parents the brothers and sisters take equal shares. If there are no surviving brothers and sisters, next in line are nephews and nieces, and when there are none the uncles and aunts are the heirs. If the nurse is married at the time of her death and has no children, her husband will inherit her entire estate. If she is married and has one child then the husband and the child will take equal shares. If she is married and has two children each gets one third. If there are more than two children the husband gets one third and the children take equal shares of the remaining two thirds. The law of intestate distribution varies from state to state so the analysis given here is a general one and may not be applicable in all states and provinces.

Dower and Curtesy

In most jurisdictions the husband and wife have a statutory right to a one-third interest in real estate owned by each other during the period of the marriage. This is the reason why a spouse always joins in signing a deed so as to give up this interest, known as dower (wife's share) or curtesy (husband's share). In some jurisdictions this has been extended to all property so that a spouse has an interest in the other's property. This interest cannot be destroyed by will or deed. This means that one spouse cannot exclude the other completely in his or her will since the statute may provide that the spouse has an interest (usually one-third) that cannot be lost through a will. This becomes important only when the nurse is married and there is an intention on the part of one spouse to exclude the other from the will.

Effect of Marriage

Most jurisdictions now have statutes which provide that an individual's will is revoked by operation of law when the individual marries. This prevents the situation of an old will signed prior to marriage taking precedence over the rights of the spouse. The law implies that the will signed before marriage was intended to be revoked at the time of marriage. If the spouse dies soon after the marriage and before preparing the new will he will be considered to have died intestate.

Wife's Will

Once it is decided that the husband needs a will, it naturally follows that the wife needs a will whether or not she has property in her own name. The reason for this is that she stands to inherit upon her husband's death and should not wait until that event occurs to prepare her will. The usual will drawn for a married man when the estate is less than $50,000 provides that everything will be left to his wife if she survives him by 90 days, and to their children or other named heirs if the wife does not survive by 90 days. This limits the probate only to the husband's estate if both die within a short time of each other. The husband's will can be a model for the wife's will, but the husband and wife should avoid joint and mutual wills, which are of questionable validity in most jurisdictions.

An important element of the wife's will is the naming of a guardian for surviving children in the event of the death of both parents. The courts are not bound by the recommendation of named guardians, but they will usually appoint the guardians as named unless there is clear evidence for avoiding the recommendations.

The Unmarried Nurse

The unmarried nurse should be familiar with the law of intestate succession in her state or province so she will know who will receive her property at the time of her death. If she wants some other result then she should have a will prepared so the property may be distributed according to her wishes.

References

1. In Re Wingham, 2 All E. R. 908.
2. In Re Denison's Estate, 162 P. 2d 245 (Wash.).

16   *Contracts*

The nurse should have a basic understanding of the law of contracts. The basis of her relation with her patients is contractual, as is her employment by a doctor or a hospital. In addition the nurse should have a basic knowledge of how contract law relates to the goods and services that she purchases on behalf of herself and her employer. In this chapter we are concerned with three general kinds of contracts: contracts between nurse and patient, contracts between nurse and employer, and contracts for the purchase of goods.

Essentials of A Contract

A contract can be defined as an agreement between two or more competent persons upon consideration to do or refrain from doing some lawful act. The definition will be more meaningful if we break it down into its six component parts: an agreement, two or more persons, competent persons, consideration, to do or refrain from doing something, lawful act. If there is no agreement there is no contract; if there is no meeting of the minds the parties have not entered into a contract. There must be two or more persons, since an individual cannot contract with himself. There must be consideration going to every party who is giving something under the contract, although a party can provide that the benefits of this consideration go to someone else. The contract may be to do some act or to refrain from doing some act. The act must be lawful, since a contract to perform an unlawful act does not constitute a binding contract.

Written, Oral, Implied, and Expressed Contracts

A contract can be written or oral, expressed or implied. A written contract is self-explanatory, since the agreement reached by the parties has been set down in writing. A written contract meeting the six tests and signed by the parties is a valid and binding contract.

The statute of frauds provides that certain contracts must be written to be enforceable. Each state has a separate statute of frauds so we can only generalize at this point. A contract for the sale of goods usually must be written to be enforceable if the value of the goods is more than $50, $100, or more depending upon the state. The statute also requires that contracts for the sale of land be in writing, as must be contracts that cannot be performed within one year. The nurse should be aware of these three important situations where the statute of frauds will not permit an oral contract to be enforceable. If one party completes his part of an oral contract, however, this takes it outside of the statute of frauds and it becomes an enforceable contract. The statute of frauds applies only to unexecuted contracts.

One of the basic misunderstandings of the written contract is that oral promises and oral terms are able to vary the terms of the written contract. The parol evidence rule states that the terms of a written contract cannot be varied by oral terms. This means that the contracting parties should write their entire contract, since one party cannot hold the other to oral promises made at the time the contract was signed. If the nurse signs a written contract, she should insist that all oral terms be added to the contract by means of an addendum clause at the end of the written contract. If she does not do so, she cannot legally force the other party to abide by the oral promises.

The most common form of contract is an oral contract in which the six essential elements are present but no written agreement is prepared. An oral contract is usually used instead of a written contract when the amount involved is small and when the parties are to immediately perform their parts of the agreement. An oral contract is just as enforceable by the courts as a written contract, the only difference being in the ability to prove the agreement arrived at by the two parties.

An oral or written agreement is an expressed agreement. The parties have discussed and stated the terms and have agreed to abide by the terms, that is, the parties have expressed themselves. In contrast to this is an implied agreement whereby there has been no discussion of a contract or an agreement between the parties but the law will still consider that an agreement exists. In many situations the law will state that an implied contract or agreement exists even though there is no expressed agreement between the parties. For example, if a patient is dying and needs a drug, and the nurse administers this expensive drug, the law will state that an agreement is implied between the patient and the nurse, whereby the patient should pay the nurse for the drug and also a fee for her services.

Another example of an implied agreement would be when a supply house sends a product to the doctor's office with a bill, and the doctor uses the product. The law would say that the doctor's use of the product, if there was no evidence of any intention of making it a gift, created an implied contract of purchase between the supply house and the doctor. Likewise, the patient entering the doctor's office for a physical examination impliedly submits himself to the examination and agrees to pay the doctor for his services, even though there is no expressed discussion of the doctor's fee.

Contracts with Patients

The relation between a doctor and his patients, or between the nurse and her patients, is a contractual one. The doctor or nurse contracts to provide professional services and the patient contracts to pay a fee for these services. In most instances the contract is an implied one. When the nurse is employed by a doctor or hospital she acts as an agent of the employer and has no contractual relation with the patient. In this instance the doctor and patient are the contracting parties and the nurse is providing services as an agent of the doctor or other employer.

The private duty nurse is the best example of the nurse who has a contractual relation with her patients. She is contracting to provide specific services for a fee. There is no reason why a nurse cannot enter into a formal written contract with the patient who employs her to provide professional services. For practical reasons this is not done, but private duty nurses may want to give some serious consideration to having written contracts with their patients.

A nurse employed to provide private duty nursing services to an aged or critically ill person is well advised to protect herself against financial loss resulting from the death of the patient. The relationship is a contractual one so the presumption is that the nurse is to be paid for her services each payment period. If the patient dies owing the nurse for one payment period there should be little or no legal difficulty in collecting from the estate. If, however, the nurse is to be paid a lump sum or is to receive a part of the estate in return for providing nursing services, she should have the contract put in writing. The courts continually say that claims against an estate for nursing services rendered under an oral contract with the deceased will not be sustained except on clear and convincing evidence. In these instances the burden is on the nurse to prove that she had a contract with the patient and that she had not been paid for her services. If she is to be paid out of the patient's estate, she should have the patient's closest relatives witness the written contract. Generally speaking, witnesses are not needed to validate a written contract, but they are highly desirable in such unusual circumstances.

Contracts with Employers

The employment of a nurse by a doctor, hospital or public institution constitutes a contract. In some instances, especially when the nurse is employed by a public institution, the employment contract is written. If we apply the six tests of the contract we find that: (1) the contracting parties are the nurse and her employer, (2) both parties are competent to contract, (3) they agree as to the services to be performed and the period for which they are to be performed, (4) the nurse provides her services in return for a salary so both parties are providing consideration, (5) they agree that the nurse will perform specific acts, and (6) these acts are legal. All the tests are met so we have a valid contract.

The tests of a valid contract should not be confused with the terms of the contract. The essential terms of a contract for the employment of a nurse are: employment period (fixed, or at the pleasure of the parties), salary (the consideration paid by the employer), duties to be performed by the nurse, fringe benefits (sick leave, insurance, vacation time, etc.), place and time of employment (working hours), and increments (agreements to change the terms of the contract as time progresses, i.e., salary increases). Even though the employment contract is not written, and even if the contract is for an unspecified period of time, the nurse should be aware of all these terms, since these are the rules she agrees to accept when she accepts the employment. A nurse seeking employment or being interviewed for a position should make a list of these terms and ask the relevant questions, so that she knows the exact terms of her employment contract. Employment contracts are the most one-sided of all contracts. The employer cannot force the employee to continue to work when she wants to quit, but the employee can force the employer to pay money damages if the contract is cancelled prematurely.

Contracts for the Purchase of Goods

The purchase of a quart of milk at the neighborhood grocery store is an example of a completed contract for the sale of milk. When the price is paid and the milk taken from the store the contract is completed. When the nurse makes purchases involving substantial amounts of money that do not immediately exchange hands, she should be careful to treat the contract with a little more attention than is warranted when she buys a quart of milk. She should remember that the oral promises made by salesmen as an inducement to purchase a product are not a part of a written contract unless they are written into that contract. She should also remember that once agreed upon, the contract is binding upon the parties even if it is not written.

In the medical office or in the hospital, when the nurse is in the position of receiving supplies for her employer, she should be aware of the implications of unordered, damaged, or nonconforming goods. When the hospital or doctor contracts for the purchase of supplies, the supplier is under an obligation to send supplies that conform to the agreement and are not in damaged condition. As an agent of the doctor or hospital the nurse binds her employer by her actions when the third party has sufficient reason to believe that the nurse has this authority. This means that if she accepts nonconforming or damaged supplies and attempts to use them on behalf of the doctor, he will be bound by her actions. The seller has breached his contract by delivering nonconforming or damaged goods, but if the nurse or the doctor accepts these goods in lieu of those ordered this amounts to an agreement to change the terms of the contract. When the nurse finds that the supplies are not what the doctor ordered or have arrived in damaged condition, she should notify the doctor and let him decide whether or not he wants to accept them. If the nurse or doctor attempts to use them they are now part of the contract. If the nurse discovers that the supplies are nonconforming or damaged when she opens the package, she should immediately close the package and not attempt to use the supplies. The same thing is true if the nurse finds that the supplies were unordered and are not samples but intended to be purchased. She should not use the unordered supplies without first conferring with the doctor. As a general rule most doctors are well advised not to accept unordered supplies since this will encourage dealers to continue this practice. If the supplies are clearly labeled as samples and it is obvious that no payment is expected, the nurse can treat them as a gift that can be accepted without responsibility.

Gifts

When one person gives another person something of value without any consideration there is a gift. Sometimes the word "gift" is erroneously used when there has been a transfer for consideration, for example, when the nurse is given a Christmas bonus at the end of the year in addition to her annual salary. For tax purposes this is considered to be additional salary for services rendered, and the gift is taxable to the nurse and deductible by the doctor. However, if the doctor presents the nurse with a non-monetary gift at the end of the year, it is not taxable income to the nurse, although it is still deductible by the doctor.

The small gift that a patient presents to the nurse on leaving the hospital is a good example of a gift that is based upon consideration. The patient is actually rewarding the nurse for services rendered, but since the patient has no legal obligation to give this reward it is a valid gift. The patient giving a gift and promising a gift are two separate matters. Once the patient has given the nurse the gift, it becomes the property of the nurse and she does not have to return it unless a court finds that she used "undue influence" to force the patient to make the gift. In this instance it would be analogous to saying that the patient did not have the mental capacity to give the gift. If the patient leaving the hospital makes a gratuitous promise to the nurse to send her a gift and fails to do so, there has been no breach of contract. A promise to present a gift is unsupported by consideration so there is no legally binding contract. The nurse cannot later enforce this gratuitous promise.

This can be contrasted to the situation in which the nurse provides special services in return for a specific sum. For example, if a nurse is asked to provide extra duty services for a patient on her own time for a promised $100, payable when the patient leaves the hospital, this $100 is not a gift because the nurse has provided consideration for the money. Thus the nurse who has provided these services can legally force the patient to fulfill his part of the contract by paying the $100.

17   *Labor Relations*

It may seem strange to find a chapter on labor relations in a book on the legal aspects of nursing, but this chapter is a necessary one. The nurse has long been in narrow straits, tightly bound by the economics of the market place and concepts of professionalism. Labor relations, the means by which an individual or group of individuals attempts to better their economic conditions, is an important means of removing the nurse from her legal and economic confines. It is, indeed, a legal aspect of nursing practice.

This chapter must of necessity include a disclaimer that it is not anti-employer, anti-doctor, or anti-hospital, because it can easily be seen that the collective bargaining segment of this chapter is a discussion of the nurse's economic and legal rights in opposition to her employer. The chapter attempts to illuminate the nurse's rights in this area without causing undue criticism or dissension. Employers, doctors, and hospitals will appreciate the nurse's interest in her own economic and legal rights that emanate from her profession, just as doctors and hospital administrators are concerned with their own economic and legal rights. At first blush it may appear that any discussion of the nurse's rights in labor relations is in contradiction to her professional status. Too often the nurse is reminded that labor relations is a matter of trade unionism and that it would be unprofessional for her to even think of labor relations within the context of nursing practice. This attitude has obviously worked to the nurse's detriment, to the point where her levels of earning have been far below those of other trained persons who have not been hindered by questions of mixing professionalism and labor relations.

It is respectfully submitted to all concerned that the subjects of professionalism and labor relations are compatible. Evidence of this is seen in the fact that hospital administrators have not hesitated to take more economically rewarding positions when available, and have not hesitated to represent themselves adequately in their bargaining for income improvements with the boards of the hospitals they serve. And there have even been instances of physicians and dentists engaging in collective bargaining when the doctors are employed by governmental units or by so-called closed panels. Surely if it is not unethical for physicians to engage in collective bargaining it is not unethical for the nursing profession to do so. It must be added parenthetically that the nurse can learn how to bargain collectively by the successful example of those employed groups of physicians who have entered into collective action for their own well-being.

Labor relations is, of course, more than collective bargaining, and collective bargaining is only a small part of the subject of labor relations for the nurse. The nurse's rights under federal and state labor relations statutes is a very important subject. However, it will be seen that many of these statutes have minimum application to the nurse and her real economic problem, the solution of which revolves around collective bargaining. The subject of labor relations falls into two broad classifications: the legal and economic rights that are provided for employed persons under the provision of state and federal law, and the economic rights that an individual can assert through the mechanism of collective bargaining.

Employment Practices

The general subject of employment practices pertains to the conditions of work imposed upon the employer because of federal and state laws. As might be expected, the employer is the one who feels the burden of statutes of this kind because they interfere with his common law rights to hire, fire, and pay whatever and however he pleases, subject only to his ability to attract and retain employees. The employee benefits from these laws since they provide him with legal rights against the employer, even to the extent that the employer is not able to fire the employee subject to the provision of state and federal law. The concept of legislation regulating employment practices is new in our society but it is apparently here to stay.

Fair Labor Standards Act

The first federal wage law was enacted by the Congress in 1938, obviously as a result of the great depression. The Fair Labor Standards Act (FLSA), popularly known as the Federal Wage and Hours Law, attempted to protect the great mass of the unemployed. The large number of unemployed gave the employer a pool from which he could draw whatever he needed at whatever price he was willing to pay. For the unemployed any wage was better than none. Thus the employer could name the wage, getting as near to one cent per hour as he dared. The first minimum wage set under the Fair Labor Standards Act was 25¢ per hour and this has been periodically increased to the current level of $1.60 per hour.

Critics of the FLSA, then and now, have maintained that setting a minimum wage hurts persons who are earning the lowest wages more than it helps them. It is sometimes argued that the minimum wage makes it uneconomical for the employer to hire anyone, so that instead of getting the sub-minimum wage the potential employee is left unemployed. Another argument long heard is that some types of employment need not be covered by the law because the individuals in these occupations do not want or need the protection of the minimum wage. The physician, for example, is clearly outside the minimum wage law, as are other professional people. Part time and short duration labor are usually outside the operation of the law. It is obviously impossible to subject the minimum wage law to the teenager who baby-sits since parent and baby-sitter would obviously both be losers if the parents were forced to pay the minimum wage.

The small business and the business that does not affect interstate and foreign commerce also remain outside the operation of the wage and hour laws. For most nurses employed in the offices of private physicians the fair labor standards act does not apply, since this is not employment covered by the FLSA. The law also exempted a number of businesses or industries that met the interstate commerce test and the dollar volume test on the basis that these businesses would have been unable to exist if they paid the minimum wage. Retail clerks, farm employees, and hospital employees were exempt on the basis that the retail store or the hospital could not stay in business if it had to pay the minimum wage. Many of these industries, hospitals included, were able to demonstrate that even if they were able to pay the minimum wage they could not meet that part of the law requiring that employees who work more than a maximum number of hours per week must be paid an overtime wage equal to one and one-half times their regular hourly rate. Hospitals were in a position to demonstrate that most hospital employees worked far in excess of the statutory number of hours, so that most employees in a hospital would become eligible for overtime pay.

Federal, state, and local governments were completely exempt from the Fair Labor Standards Act's minimum wage provisions, except for states and their political subdivisions insofar as coverage of hospitals, nursing homes, and a few others were concerned. This was construed to mean that employees of state or municipal hospitals who would otherwise be outside the Act as state employees were now granted coverage under the FLSA. This did not mean that the Fair Labor Standards Act applied to all hospital employees or even in the same way that it applied to employees of other industries of businesses.

In 1966, however, the Fair Labor Standards Act was amended to remove from the list of exemptions all nursing homes and hospitals. Now FLSA coverage applies whether the hospital is public or private, and whether the hospital is operated on a profit or nonprofit basis. Physicians are still specifically exempt under the law and are given no protection. Practically speaking, this is not meaningful since it is doubtful that physicians employed in a hospital are being paid at salary levels below the minimum wage. This raises the point that the law really has no application to the employees who are already being paid wages in excess of the minimum wage, with one exception. As the minimum wage is increased or imposed in a business or hospital for the first time it has the effect of sending all wage levels up. As the lowest paid individual gets an increase the higher paid employee sees less of a wage differential between himself and the lowest paid, and he naturally wishes to retain the differential. This spiraling effect, which is often a major criticism invoked against the minimum wage law, is perhaps one of the major benefits of the law. Economists argue from both sides of this question, some saying that this benefits all low priced labor and others claiming that it merely causes inflation. The latter argue that by raising the minimum wage, all wages go up proportionately, which raise prices in a proportionate amount. The end result is that everything has increased with little or no gain for anyone.

Hospitals are placed in a slightly better position than other employers when it comes to overtime pay. The hospital has the benefit of the more lenient standards which require the premium overtime pay only for those hours in excess of 44 hours a week until February 1, 1968 and only for hours in excess of 42 hours per week until February 1, 1969. In addition the hospital and its employees can enter into an agreement to make a fourteen day period the basis for overtime computation, instead of the usual seven day period. This provision was adopted in light of the prevailing practice of hospital employees, especially nurses, to work seven or eight consecutive days and then have several days off. Without this special provision the hospitals would have to pay overtime to most nurses or change the current practices so that nurses would not be working more than the maximum nonpremium hours per week.

The advent of the operation of the minimum wage provision to hospitals has real meaning only to those employees who were earning less than the minimum wage, except for the spiral effect mentioned earlier. However, the portion of the law providing for time and one-half for overtime could have some real impact upon those nurses who are already earning in excess of the minimum wage.

When the law was made applicable to hospitals it was done so on the basis of new employees. For the purposes of the Fair Labor Standards Act all covered hospital employees were considered to be new employees. To the hospitals the treatment of all employees as new employees resulted in a substantial immediate financial savings. According to the 1966 amendments the minimum wage for currently employed employees is $1.60 per hour effective February 1, 1968. For all employees newly covered under the 1966 amendments the minimum wage is $1 per hour effective February 1, 1967 plus an increase of 15¢ per year as of February 1 of each year until the minimum wage reaches $1.60 on February 1, 1968.

It is likely that most professional nurses will benefit only from the impact of the overtime provisions of the law. Many practical nurses may benefit by the imposition of the minimum wage. There are special provisions limiting the benefits of the overtime rates to individuals employed in nursing homes. Generally these employees do not get the benefits of the requirement that employees must receive one and one half times the usual rate for extra hours.

A continuing major exemption or special class under the law is for students. A teaching hospital could get a certificate under the law which constitutes permission to pay student nurses less than the minimum wage. The law recognizes the possible need for using student nurses as salaried employees as part of the teaching process, and an attempt is made to compromise so as not to make it impossible to utilize the services of student nurses.

COVERAGE FOR NURSES. As pointed out earlier physicians are specifically excluded from the law. However, this specific exclusion also states that it has no application to nurses, which leaves open the question of whether or not practical and professional nurses are included under the FLSA. Even though hospitals are now covered under the FLSA, those employees who are considered to be executive, administrative, and professional within the meaning of the white collar exclusion are still exempt from the minimum wage, equal pay, and overtime pay provisions of the FLSA. Since the white collar exemption depends upon the nature of the duties performed by the individual employee, there is no general exclusion or non-exclusion for professional or practical nurses. The burden is upon the employer to prove that the employee is exempt from the act. Naturally the employee does not want to be exempt if he is in a low income category. To be exempt as a professional employee, the nurse generally must be earning $115 or more per week, she must be performing work that is predominately intellectual and varied (not routine) that cannot be standardized in point of time, and she must be performing work that requires specific and specialized skills as distinguished from apprentice training and training for routine work. The professional nurse, and perhaps more important the practical nurse, may feel that as a professional person she meets this test and is exempt from the Act. At the same time it is in the best interests of the underpaid nurse to be considered a nonprofessional so that she is included under the Act. In any event the burden is upon the employer to establish that the employee is not covered. The question of whether or not a nurse is protected must be answered on an individual basis. Nurses in a supervisory position in a hospital undoubtedly do not come under the protection of the law, nor would they need its protection. Little information can be found in the law on the question of whether or not the nurse is exempt as a professional person. Only since the 1966 amendments to the FLSA have any but a handful of nurses (industrial nurses) been subject to the law. It is very likely that the courts will have to determine whether nurses, especially practical nurses, fall within the definition of professionals as used in this law.

INDUSTRIAL NURSES. Industrial nurses were eligible for coverage under the Fair Labor Standards Act long before the 1966 amendments if they were in a business covered under the Act and not subject to the exemption granted in the case of administrative, supervisory, and professional personnel. We recall that the Act applies only when the business has more than a minimum amount of sales and only when the business affects interstate or foreign commerce. The activities of an industrial nurse do not ordinarily affect interstate or foreign commerce, but the Act does provide coverage for employees whose work is closely related and directly essential to the production of goods intended for interstate commerce. In most instances, if the business is subject to the FLSA, the industrial nurse employed thereby is also covered. The interpretation of the law is that if the nurse's activities are essential to production, she is covered.

Civil Rights Acts

It was not until February 10, 1964 that the Congress passed the first Fair Employment Practices Act, as part of the Civil Rights Act of 1964. This portion is now known as Title VII. Title VII prohibits discrimination on the basis of race, color, religion, sex, or national origin by employers, unions, and employment agencies. An employer violates the Civil Rights Act if, on the basis of race, color, religion, sex, or national origin, he fails to hire, fires, segregates employees in a manner adversely affecting their status as employees, or otherwise discriminates in compensation, terms, conditions, or privileges of employment.

The provisions of the Civil Rights Act apply to employers engaged in any industry affecting commerce. It is also clear that the Congress intends that this law be applied to hospitals, and this is also made clear by a number of opinions issued by the General Counsel of the Equal Employment Opportunity Commission. An opinion issued by the General Counsel in a letter dated December 1, 1965 states that a private hospital which employs 100 or more persons is subject to Title VII of the Civil Rights Act. In an opinion issued a few days later on December 8, 1965 the General Counsel stated that Title VII applies to voluntary nonprofit hospitals that are not owned by the federal government, or by state governments or political subdivisions thereof. This means that the Civil Rights Act would apply only to those nurses employed in other than state or municipally owned hospitals.

The authority in the Civil Rights Act to prohibit discrimination extends also to any hospital receiving federal funds. In an address before the American Hospital Association, an assistant secretary of the Department of Health, Education and Welfare stated that the ending of employment discrimination in hospitals receiving federal funds is a principle objective of the Department of Health, Education and Welfare's program of compliance with Title VI of the Civil Rights Act of 1964. Title VI authorizes federal agencies to cut off funds for federally supported institutions that practice discrimination. A Department official said specifically that "it (Title VI) means that all training programs for nurses, interns, residents, licensed practical nurses, and orderlies must be available to all on a nondiscriminatory basis."

The Civil Rights Act specifically excludes the United States Government as an employer, but the act states that it is the policy of the government to insure equal employment opportunities for federal employees without distinction. The Civil Service Commission and the individual federal agencies bar discrimination in federal employment in accordance with an executive order (11246).

The Civil Rights Act provides a partial exemption in the case of religious organizations. In an opinion letter dated October 20, 1965 the General Counsel stated that if a denominational hospital qualifies as a "religious corporation, association or society" within the meaning of the Civil Rights Act, it is exempt from coverage with respect to those employees who perform work connected with the hospital's religious activities. In general, however, the functions of a hospital do not include religious activities, and few if any of its employees would be exempt from coverage under the Act. In August of the following year the General Counsel issued an opinion stating that a Catholic hospital would probably violate Title VII of the Equal Employment Opportunities Act by refusing to hire other than Catholic nurses. Title VII exempts religious institutions only with respect to employees who perform work connected with religious activities and the functions of a hospital nurse do not generally involve religious activities. From these opinions issued by the General Counsel it seems clear that nurses employed in religious institutions that are otherwise covered under the Civil Rights Law retain this coverage, notwithstanding the fact that the employer is a religious institution.

Most nurses employed in private offices will find that the federal Civil Rights Law does not directly apply to their employment. The private office will undoubtedly not be affected by the federal law inasmuch as the minimum number of employees (25 after July 1, 1968) are probably not present and the practice does not affect commerce.

The Civil Rights Act, which is a federal law, does not preëmpt state law in this field. In fact Congress has encouraged the operation of state laws on this subject where they exist. New York was the first state to enact a law (1945) forbidding discrimination in private employment. Most states have enacted fair employment practice laws prohibiting discrimination in employment on account of race, color, creed, or national origin. A few laws also include national ancestry, sex, and age. Thirty-eight states and the District of Columbia have Fair Employment Practice Acts. In addition, a number of municipalities have enacted ordinances prohibiting employment discrimination based upon race or other grounds.

If the nurse believes that she has been subject to discrimination in employment practices she must decide whether her recourse lies in contacting a state or federal agency. If the nurse has been employed in a private office it is most likely that her recourse lies with the state agency. A hospital employed nurse can easily assume that the coverage is available through the federal government's local office for equal employment opportunities. If she contacts the wrong agency she will most likely be referred to the appropriate one.

Age Discrimination

In enacting Title VII of the Civil Rights Act the question of whether age discrimination should be made an unlawful employment practice was raised and rejected, but was expressly reserved for future consideration. The federal law does not prohibit an employer from discrimination based on age, nor does it bar him from discharging an employee because of his age. Under federal law it is still lawful for an employer to limit his hiring to employees over a certain age and then refuse to hire employees who have passed a certain age. Nor is it unlawful for an employer to discharge an employee in order to replace him with a younger person.

However 26 states have enacted laws that do prohibit discrimination because of age. These state laws do not always apply to all employees and all employers. For example, the California law prohibits age discrimination only when an employer has six or more employees. The California law provides that it shall be unlawful for an employer to refuse to hire, discharge, or demote any individual between 40 and 64 solely on the grounds of age. The California law is typical, although some of the other states have different limitations or apply to all employers regardless of the number of employees.

The nurse who feels that she has been subject to discrimination because of her age should seek her recourse by contacting the appropriate state agency, although she must realize that in approximately one-half of the states the law provides no protection against this form of discrimination.

Summary

The discussion of labor relations has been limited to the statutory protection that the nurse enjoys as an employee. This protection issues from acts of the state and federal legislatures that were enacted to protect employees by providing them with a minimal level of income, and to protect them from discriminatory employment practices. The anti-discrimination protection is not complete because not all employment situations are covered and the protection does not apply to all instances. The protection of the minimum wage law has been recently extended to the nurse and other hospital employees, and provides only minimal protection and then only for those nurses who have been receiving less than minimum salaries specified in the federal law. For the majority of nurses, practical as well as professional, the minimum wage law does not solve the problem of wages because their wages have been greater than the federally set minimum but still not commensurate with the skill and training they possess or the services which they perform. This brings us to the subject of collective bargaining.

Collective Bargaining

The concept of collective bargaining is not a new idea; its newness lies in its application to the nursing profession. The labor law is relatively complicated and has had little general application to the nursing profession. The labor law has usually excluded the nurse from its operation as either a professional or administrative employee, and there has been little in the way of unionization of nurses or the establishment of collective bargaining units of nurses under the appropriate sections of the National Labor Relations Act. Nurses have generally avoided this formal and legalistic approach for many reasons, not the least of which has been the traditional concept of professionalism. Yet the nurse does have certain legal and economic rights, and she is not prohibited from exercising these rights merely because she is engaged in the practice of a profession. Collective bargaining in a somewhat less formal (from a legal viewpoint) manner would seem to be tailor-made for the nurse employed in a hospital. It would seem to have little application to the industrial nurse or the nurse in a private office.

The theory behind collective bargaining has always been that group action by employees is more effective than individual action. An employee who is disgruntled with wages and working conditions could find himself discharged for complaining, while another worker is ready and willing to take the now vacant position at the same or lower salary level. The employee who takes it upon himself to be a spokesman for all employees in an effort to change working conditions or wage levels might find himself unemployed for his efforts, or he might find that although his efforts were successful he was still discharged as being a disruptive influence.

Collective bargaining means that a group of similarly situated individuals agree to stand or fall as a group. They present their demands to their common employer and then offer their alternatives. If the group disunites then there is no collective bargaining. Consider the situation where all 100 employees ask an employer for a raise at one time as opposed to a single employee asking for a salary increase with each, the 100 and the individual, threatening to quit at the time the demand is made. The individual could more easily be fired than the group, for obvious reasons.

Collective bargaining can be an effective force for bringing wages and working conditions to an acceptable level. Historically it has been a successful mechanism, held to be in the public interest. However collective bargaining by employees can also create the situation in which the employer has no alternative but to close his business or pay wages that are disproportionate to services and income. This was the general reason for the enactment of federal and state labor laws that stand between management and labor to prevent misuse of collective bargaining.

There is little opportunity for the nurse in the private office or industry to participate in collective bargaining because of the very nature of this activity. Even if there are a number of nurses in the office willing to participate in this concerted activity, they have no protection by state or federal law, and there is the distinct possibility that the doctor or doctors will resort to discharging the employees rather than acceding to their demands. There is nothing in the federal law that says a group of physicians in practice together have to accept the terms demanded by a group of nurses acting in concert. In addition, the nature of the private office would make it unlikely that the necessary doctor-nurse relation could exist after an attempt was made at collective bargaining. The nurse employed by business has no recourse to collective bargaining because there is usually no one available for her to "collect" with. The labor laws are very strict with respect to bargaining units and the solo nurse (or two or three) employed in a business is not permitted to participate in the bargaining unit of other employees who do not fit into the same category.

It is probably legally possible for a group of nurses employed in a single hospital or group of hospitals to formalize a collective bargaining unit under the applicable state or federal law. However a more likely response to the issue might be the recognition of the state nurses' association as the representative of the nurses. This less legalistic approach is probably desirable inasmuch as the nurse is considering bargaining against a state or nonprofit hospital, and because there is some doubt as to whether the federal and state labor laws are applicable in such a situation. This informal method of collective bargaining is less binding upon the participating nurses, and only those nurses who voluntarily participate in the collective bargaining will be morally bound. In most instances the collective bargaining unit legally recognizes bargains for all persons in the unit whether or not they agree with the majority position.

The usual method for informal collective bargaining is for the nurses in a given hospital or group of hospitals to serve notice that they intend to resign at a specified date unless certain employment terms are altered. The nurses then agree among themselves that their nurses' association will be their bargaining agent and if the association agrees to assume this responsibility there is collective bargaining. There have been a number of concerted activities conducted by the California Nurses' Association within the past few years that have been highly successful and illustrate this method of collective action. In the San Francisco area some 3,000 nurses in hospitals threatened a mass resignation. This strike was averted by the hospital administrator and the nurses agreeing to submit differences to a fact finding committee appointed by the governor. In this case an interim agreement was accepted by the nurses by a narrow vote. It is interesting to note that there were 3,000 nurses involved in this situation and only 1,500 showed up at the meeting to consider whether or not to accept the interim agreement. Furthermore, many of the 1,500 did not vote at the meeting. It is a matter for some conjecture why so few attended the meeting and why many who attended failed to vote. The interim agreement raised nurses' salaries by $70 to $75 per month. The nurses asked for increases of $236 to $311 per month and the hospital offered $45 a month immediately and $105 a month over a three year period.

One of the benefits of the nurses' association acting as the spokesman and unifying agent is the minimization of reprisals against the individuals who speak for the nurses. If the nurses use a committee of their own number as their spokesmen, it is possible that the individuals who serve on this committee will suffer personal reprisals in their later employment. One of the essential elements of any collective bargaining agreement is the stipulation that there will not be economic or other employment reprisals against the spokesmen or leaders of the nurses.

It might be worthwhile considering two other situations in which the California Nurses' Association acted as the bargaining agent for groups of nurses. In August, 1966, nurses reported in sick and three city hospitals in San Francisco reached an agreement with the Nurses' Association. The result was a salary increase from $113 to $138 per month for some 800 nurses and maintenance of the traditional 15% differential over private hospitals. In southern California the California Nurses' Association represented 14,000 nurses and achieved a 25% salary increase. Wage increases averaged $130 per month and brought salary levels to $6,600 for new graduates and $10,500 for supervisory nurses.

The recitation of the success of the collective bargaining conducted by some California nurses should not be construed as a suggestion that all nurses immediately consider the possibilities of similar action. The purpose of this chapter is to describe the nurse's rights in collective bargaining and other aspects of labor relations without recommending a particular course of action. The threat of mass resignations or of large groups calling in sick presents a number of legal and ethical problems that should not be taken lightly. The agreement by a group of nurses to enter into concerted activity of this kind could be construed to be in violation of state and federal law. Nurses contemplating such action should consult with their nurses' association and obtain legal counsel before any action is taken. There is also the problem of the hospital accepting the threat and permitting the nurses to resign. This puts the ethical burden on the nurse for leaving patients unattended in hospitals. The potential salary increases for nurses utilizing the collective bargaining system are substantial, but they are small compared to the enormous legal and ethical problems which can be presented. This is even more reason for the nurses contemplating action of this sort to consult with their nurses' association and obtain legal counsel before any action is taken.

The traditionally low salaries offered to nurses employed in hospitals does not aid in decreasing the shortage of nurses in the labor force. Too often nurses are expected to sacrifice their personal financial security for the privilege of honoring their moral creed to serve their patients. Those nurses and nurses' associations that contemplate collective bargaining serve more than their own financial self-interest. By improving the conditions of employment and the economic well-being of the professional and practical nurse, they are making nursing more attractive as a career. The major hospital problem, shortage of nurses, may find its solution in the improvement of the economic conditions of the hospital nurse.

In a mimeographed booklet released by the American Nurses' Association in early 1967, "Data on American Nurses' Association," the programs and activities of that organization are listed. Under the title Economic and General Welfare appears the following statement:

> ANA promotes the economic and general welfare of nurses as it directly affects the recruitment and efficiency of nursing personnel. Almost all state nurses associations have adopted an economic security program and may represent nurses in negotiating salaries, hours, and other employment conditions with employers. Although the association maintains a no-strike policy, by negotiating with employers they seek to insure employment conditions that will attract young people to the profession and retain nurses in practice.

The American Nurses' Association has also developed a Commission on Economic and General Welfare, which has the responsibility of developing and implementing economic standards, basic principles of desirable employment conditions, and a program of economic education. The commission studies and evaluates the economics of nursing, and also gives advice and assistance to state nurses' associations.

The following excerpt is from the pamphlet "Economically Speaking Are You Talking to Yourself?" published by the Economic Security Program of the American Nurses' Association.

Nurses, when they do things together, act effectively.
Nurses in local units, working with state nurses' associations, bargain with employers about:

> equal employment opportunities
> higher salaries
> regular wage increases
> shift rotation
> shift differentials
> health benefits
> retirement plans
> longer vacations
> in-service educational programs
> grievance machinery.

Nurses in public employment, working through their state nurses' association, present their needs and concerns to:

> state civil service commissions
> county health departments
> legislators
> city departments of hospitals
> health commissioners
> budget administrators.

ANA and SNA's support legislation that promotes and protects nurses' welfare. Achievements include:

> collective bargaining rights for nurses
> workmen's compensation coverage of staphylococcal infections
> minimum wage and hours laws
> social security coverage for government employees.

18 *Workmen's Compensation*

Workmen's compensation is a combination of insurance and social insurance designed to protect the worker against the hazards that exist in his particular occupation. Philosophically, workmen's compensation is an attempt to have the consumer bear the cost of compensating the employee who has been injured if the injury occurred in the course of employment. The employer pays for workmen's compensation insurance and ostensibly passes the costs to his patients, clients, or customers, so that ultimately the user of the product or service pays the cost of caring for the employee who is injured in the production of the goods or services. Because of the complicated nature of workmen's compensation, the general application of these laws will be discussed before their application to the nurse is demonstrated.

Theory of Workmen's Compensation

If the doctor has injured his patients through his own negligence, he is guilty of malpractice and can rely upon his malpractice insurance policy for protection. The patient has the right to sue, and must usually prove injury, negligent conduct on the part of the doctor, and proximate cause. Under our system of law, if the patient can prove these three elements of the malpractice case he wins a judgment that is theoretically equal to the injury suffered.

What if the injured person is an employee of the doctor rather than a patient? Without the workmen's compensation laws the injured employee would be in the unenviable position of having to bring a lawsuit against his employer, and would have to prove that his employer was negligent and that the negligence caused the injury. The questions of the employee's own negligence and whether or not he assumed the risk of his occupation when he took the employment may further complicate the issue.

From the employee's point of view the workmen's compensation laws make it unnecessary for him to sue his employer, and often do away with the need for him to retain an attorney. He can usually collect all of his benefits without incurring legal fees. When an injured party is being recompensed for his injury it must usually be shown that there has been negligent conduct on the part of the person who is being sued. This is not so in the workmen's compensation situation. The employer is liable under the workmen's compensation laws without any question of negligence. The employee can recover for his injury by merely showing that he has been injured and that the injury was received in the course of his performing the duties of his employment.

This imposition of vicarious liability (liability without fault) may seem to be unduly hard on the employer. However, there are two distinct factors in the workmen's compensation laws that make the laws attractive to the employer. First, the workmen's compensation laws set a maximum on the amount of recovery the employee can obtain. This maximum is usually quite a bit lower than what an injured employee could expect to receive if there were no workmen's compensation laws. Second, the employee has no choice but to receive his benefits under the workmen's compensation laws; he cannot bring a separate legal action against his employer.

The workmen's compensation system, then, is a means of providing redress to the injured employee at minimum cost to his employer and in such a manner as to preserve the continuation of the employment relationship. This system fixes the compensation for the injured employee, not on the usual indemnity basis applicable in a malpractice lawsuit, but on the principle of a division of loss between the employer and employee, and the amount of the compensation, subject to a maximum, relates to the average earnings of the employee.

Workmen's Compensation Laws

Since each state has the power to enact its own workmen's compensation law, we have fifty state laws, a law for the District of Columbia, one for Puerto Rico and one enacted by Congress for federal employees. There is considerable variation among the states in their workmen's compensation laws, in the types of coverage, the persons and types of employees covered, the kinds and causes of compensable injuries, and so forth. In addition, meetings of the state legislatures usually result in some amendments to the laws, to remove newly discovered defects or to meet changing political needs.

Compulsory and Elective Systems

In slightly more than half of the states workmen's compensation is compulsory, and the law becomes effective when the employment relation commences. Other states maintain an elective system whereby the employer and employee can accept or reject the benefits of the act. However, these elective states discourage the employer from rejecting workmen's compensation, because the employer is usually prohibited from defending himself in the usual legal manner if he is sued by an employee for an injury that occurs during the course of employment.

Perhaps under the assumption that the small business has a better safety record or that the employer can defend himself in the small business situation, most states exempt businesses (including professional ones) not having a minimum number of employees. The laws generally exempt agricultural and migratory workers, and some exempt employees of nonprofit organizations. All states have some provision, in varying degrees, for exempting public employees.

Insurance for the Employer

When an employer makes his payments for workmen's compensation insurance he exhausts his liability, whether or not an employee is injured. This insurance can be financed in different ways, depending on the state. The employer may pay a tax directly to the state, or he may be insured by a state approved private insurance company. If the employer is able to show sufficient financial strength he can be self-insured.

In some states if the employer has made his premium payments to an insurance company the employee's only recourse is against that company, and he cannot bring action against the employer. In most states, however, the employee can bring action against both the insurance company and his employer, and the only way the employer could have any liability would be if the insurance company defaults.

Employment Relation

For the workmen's compensation laws to be in effect an employment relation must clearly exist, in fact as well as in name. The injury must be attributable to the employment and must be of the kind generally described in the state law. For the nurse this raises the issue of whether or not she was, in fact, the doctor's employee or an independent contractor. The usual test is direction and control. If the doctor has the right to direct the nurse in the course of her work, an employment relationship exists.

Usually the nurse, dental assistant, dental hygienist, or technician working in the doctor's office or hospital would be considered an employee. There could be a complicating factor in the case of a shared employee, such as a receptionist working for a number of doctors in a common reception room. This situation should be taken care of by determining in advance whose employee she is and then providing adequate insurance coverage. As a general rule if the courts cannot determine whether the relation is one of employee or independent contractor, the doubt will be resolved in favor of a finding that an employment relation existed.

Employee Benefits

The benefits an employee is entitled to receive are usually stated in terms of a percentage of his average wage, for a specified number of weeks. Disability benefits, loss of limb benefits, burial benefits, and survivors' benefits can enure to the benefit of an employee who is covered and whose injury falls within the classification of being insured under a workmen's compensation program.

If the employee is disabled some states will provide weekly benefits for life, while others will provide that benefits are payable only for a stated period of time. The amount of the benefit can range from as low as 55% of average weekly wages in Alabama and Idaho to a high of 97½% of average weekly wages in Illinois. Most states provide for one-half to two-thirds of the average weekly wages. In addition, some states have a maximum amount of total benefits with the lows being $10,000 in Georgia and North and South Carolina. In Oregon the injured employee can get benefits from the first day of disability. In the other states the employee does not receive benefits for a waiting period of up to seven days.

The workmen's compensation laws also provide for medical benefits for injured employees and for certain expenditures for rehabilitation. The employee has the obligation of telling the employer of the injury within a specified number of days of the injury, and he must file his claim within a stated period of time.

In many states if there is an illegally employed minor and the minor is injured compensation is increased as a penalty. In about one-third of the states the minor gets double compensation and in Wisconsin the minor gets triple compensation. In some of these states the employer has to make these additional payments out of his own pocket. Another interesting point is that in most states the attorney's fee for assisting the employee in collecting his benefits is subject to board or judicial review and an unacceptable fee is disallowed.

The employee does not receive benefits in all cases of injury received while in the course of employment. If the injury is caused by the employees own willful conduct, or results from intoxication or total disregard for his own safety, the court or the board may disallow the claim. The workmen's compensation laws also provide for an exclusion for "horseplay" and most will not allow benefits when this is the cause of the injury.

The Nurse and Workmen's Compensation

From the nurse's point of view the workmen's compensation law provides the assurance that she will receive some income if she is disabled because of an injury suffered during the course of her employment. Most nurses will agree that this form of protection against on the job injuries is distinctly more attractive than suing the doctor, hospital, or government agency employing her. However, the nurse cannot always assume that her employment by a doctor or hospital comes under the coverage of the state workmen's compensation law. She may be excluded for any of the following reasons: The doctor may not employ the minimum number of employees required for coverage. The state law may apply only to hazardous occupations. State law may exempt nonprofit employers (hospitals). Law may permit voluntary coverage but this election is not always made. Governmental agencies may be exempt. In addition, some state laws exempt persons who are in an executive or supervisory capacity. This may mean that the head nurse or supervisor in a large group practice or a hospital does not come under the protection of the law.

There have been relatively few lawsuits brought by nurses to establish their eligibility for benefits under the workmen's compensation laws, in spite of the fact that workmen's compensation is probably the most common subject coming before the courts. This undoubtedly stems from the fact that people do not even consider workmen's compensation and whether or not they are covered until an injury has been suffered. In a recent court decision involving a nurse in a workmen's compensation case the Supreme Court of Colorado held that a public health nurse who was employed by the City of Denver and whose duties included close physical contact with individuals infected with beta streptococcus, was entitled to a workmen's compensation award when she became infected by this organism.[1] It is interesting to note that in this case the nurse was entitled to the maximum benefits under the law of Colorado, $40.25 per week during her period of disability.

Another workmen's compensation claim brought by a nurse was barred by the statute of limitations. The nurse injured her back while turning patients in bed in a hospital. She was hospitalized about one month after the injury and she brought her workmen's compensation claim one day less than a year from the time she was hospitalized, but more than 13 months from the time of injury. The Tennessee Supreme Court[2] held that the one year statute of limitations for filing workmen's compensation claims starts to run from the time the worker was injured, and the failure of the nurse to file the claim within this period destroyed her right to benefits under the law of that state. The lesson from this decision is clear. The nurse who suffers an injury during the course of her employment should file her workmen's compensation claim as soon as possible after the injury occurs.

The workmen's compensation law may prevent a nurse from bringing a legal action for negligence against the hospital that employs her. Yet there are a number of instances in which the nurse can sue the hospital-employer. The most obvious situation is where the workmen's compensation law does not apply. Then the nurse can sue the hospital in the same manner that she can sue any negligent party who causes her injury. The nurse can also sue the hospital if she is not an employee of the hospital, for example if she enters the hospital to assist her doctor-employer and is injured due to the negligence of the hospital. In this situation the nurse is an employee of the doctor and not of the hospital and the workmen's compensation statute does not apply. If the nurse is a student nurse or a volunteer in a hospital, the nurse is not bound by the operation of the workmen's compensation law since a true employment relation does not exist.

The hospital has a legal duty toward all its employees, as well as toward visitors and patients, to maintain the hospital as a safe place for invitees. The visitors and patients have the usual recourse in the event they are injured due to the hospital's negligence, and the nurse has the right to sue to the extent that she is not an employee. In a recently reported case a nurse's aide was held to have a cause of action against a hospital when she contracted a hemolytic staphylococcus infection while working in a nursery for premature infants. She alleged that the hospital had a duty toward her to provide her with a safe place in which to work, that it negligently breached this duty, and that the negligence was the proximate cause of her having contracted the infection. According to the Georgia appellate court these allegations stated a cause of action sufficient to raise the issues of negligence and proximate cause for submission to a jury.[3]

When the nurse is in a hospital as a patient and not a nurse the workmen's compensation statute clearly does not apply. A student nurse was hospitalized as a patient and was held to have a cause of action against the hospital, according to another Georgia court, when she developed thrombophlebitis following the administration of a BSP test. The student nurse had consulted a hospital resident about abdominal pains. He ordered a BSP test, which was administered by a hospital technician. In her lawsuit against the hospital the nurse alleged that the technician was an employee of the hospital and not of the resident, and that the technician was unqualified and administered the test in a negligent fashion. Although the resulting injuries were only medical probabilities and possibilities, the court said she had a cause of action against the hospital because these probabilities and possibilities caused her mental pain and suffering.[4]

References

1. City and County of Denver v. Pollard, 417 P. 2d 231 (Colo. 1966).
2. Watkins v. Home Indemnity Co., 409 S.W. 2d 359 (Tenn. 1966).
3. Thigpen v. Executive Committee of the Baptist Convention of the State of Georgia, 152 S.E. 2d 920 (Ga. 1966).
4. Mull v. Emory University, Inc., 150 S.E. 2d 276 (Ga. 1966).

19 *Insurance and Retirement Programs for the Nurse*

Appended to this chapter is a list of the basic insurance needs of a nurse. The individual nurse may or may not need all the insurance mentioned on this list. A quick review of the check list may give her the impression that her sole purpose for practicing nursing is to meet insurance premiums as they fall due. Admittedly, adequate insurance coverage is expensive, but it is submitted that insurance is inexpensive when the alternatives are considered.

The Insurance Broker

If the nurse wishes to devote a minimum of time to insurance coverage and get the necessary coverage at the least cost, she should consider contacting an insurance broker. An insurance broker is one who is engaged in the business of procuring insurance for persons who apply to him for that service. Acting as a middleman between the nurse and the various insurance companies, he is not employed by any one of them although he does receive his payments in the form of a commission from the insurance company. The insurance broker is the agent of the individual purchasing insurance, and conducts a private practice for his clients not unlike those conducted by other professional persons.

In addition to actually purchasing insurance for the nurse, the broker will counsel her as to her insurance needs and help her in the selection of acceptable insurance companies. He will periodically review the nurse's insurance coverage to establish that it is current. He can arrange to receive the premium notices, and in turn bill the nurse, which will result in a substantial decrease in the nurse's desk work. By placing all her insurance

140

through one broker, the nurse becomes an important account and can expect her broker's continued advice and loyalty. Insurance brokers are licensed in most states and the nurse should select her broker as carefully as she would her attorney, accountant, or physician.

Kinds of Insurance

Malpractice Insurance

Malpractice insurance, sometimes referred to as professional responsibility or professional liability insurance, protects the nurse against claims of negligent conduct arising from professional activities.

THE NEED FOR MALPRACTICE INSURANCE. In its simplest form, the question of whether or not the nurse needs malpractice insurance would have to be answered in the affirmative. Usually, if the nurse works under the direction and control of a doctor he is legally liable for her negligent conduct under *respondeat superior*. The nurse's negligence in performing her official duties as a hospital employee will similarly render the hospital liable for her actions. But this does not mean that the nurse cannot also be sued for her negligent conduct. When the law imposes liability on the employer for the negligent acts of his employees, the employee does not escape legal liability for her acts. The effect of *respondeat superior* is to permit the injured party to select an additional person to sue. The fact that the patient has two persons to sue, i.e., doctor and nurse or hospital and nurse, does not mean that the patient can recover twice for one injury. In most instances the patient will be limited to one recovery. A lawsuit against a doctor for the negligent acts of his nurse which results in a judgment against the doctor will, under most circumstances, protect the nurse against a subsequent lawsuit. It is at this final stage that the nurse may be protected because of legal action taken against her employer.

Most doctors have malpractice coverage that protects them if they are sued for the negligent actions of one of their employees. But the doctor's malpractice insurance does not afford protection for the employee. If the court holds the doctor liable on the basis of *respondeat superior*, the doctor's insurance protects him. If the court finds that the nurse was liable the doctor's coverage provides her no protection. More important, if the nurse is sued individually or in conjunction with the hospital or doctor, she will need her own insurance protection to provide for her defense. The injured patient may decide to sue the doctor, the nurse, or both for the nurse's negligent act. In the event the doctor and the nurse are sued in the same lawsuit the doctor's insurance company will probably be willing to defend the doctor and the nurse at no cost to the nurse. However, the doctor and the nurse may not have identical interests in the lawsuit so the nurse wants her own representation and this can be secured only by purchasing her own malpractice insurance policy or by retaining an attorney at the time she is sued. It is obviously more expedient to purchase the insurance.

The nurse who assumes that the doctor's insurance coverage provides her with enough protection is making a substantial error, one that won't come to mind until she needs the coverage most—when she is sued. It can be assumed that most patients will sue the doctor for the nurse's actions rather than sue the nurse directly, but this does not help the nurse who is sued. The following are examples of instances when the doctor's or the hospital's insurance are not sufficient to protect the nurse. If the hospital is protected under the doctrine of charitable immunity and cannot be sued, it can be assumed that the patient will sue the nurse. If the patient has a favorable relationship with his doctor and does not wish to endanger this relationship, he may sue the nurse and not the doctor. Sometimes the doctor cannot be located for the purposes of gaining jurisdiction. If the nurse is a private duty nurse or otherwise does not work under the direction and control of a doctor, she alone is liable for her actions.

Some hospitals provide coverage for the nurse in the event that she is sued for her negligent acts while working in the hospital. This coverage names the nurse as one of the insureds so the hospital is indirectly buying a malpractice insurance policy for her. Although this is obviously beneficial to the nurse she should not rely on this insurance. She may not be working in one of the hospitals which provides this benefit of employment or the coverage provided under the hospital's insurance program may not be sufficient in amount or scope.

When the costs of malpractice insurance are compared to the potential loss in the event of a lawsuit the obvious answer is for the nurse to purchase her own malpractice insurance. It might be added, parenthetically, that the small cost of the malpractice insurance is further reduced by the fact that this is deductible for federal income tax purposes as an ordinary and necessary expense of engaging in nursing practice.

WHEN IS MALPRACTICE INSURANCE NEEDED? A nurse needs malpractice insurance from the time she sees her first patient, which may be before she is licensed. Since student nurses have been sued, it may even be desirable for the student nurse to be insured. A nurse need not continue malpractice insurance after she has ceased to engage in nursing. The malpractice insurance policy provides protection for the period for which it was purchased. Therefore, if the nurse has left practice and no longer has insurance she is protected if sued because of some injury that occurred when she was in practice and had insurance.

If the nurse leaves active practice and devotes her time to administrative duties in nursing, there is no need for her to continue her malpractice insurance unless her administrative position requires that she exert some direction or control over other nurses. If she has authority to direct and control other nurses she should maintain her malpractice insurance since she may be legally liable for her actions in directing other nurses, or she may be liable for the actions of the other nurses on the basis of *respondeat superior.*

WHO IS COVERED? The nurse is obviously a named insured under her own malpractice policy. She wants coverage for liability arising out of her own actions and coverage for her liability for actions of those persons for whom she is responsible. As pointed out earlier, the employer is legally liable for the negligent acts of the employees committed in furtherance of the employment relationship. Although the terms employer and employee are often used to establish this liability, there need not be an employer-employee relation for the master to be liable for the servant. In this sense the nurse is liable for the actions of these persons for whom she has the authority to direct and control, which makes the head nurse or supervising nurse liable for the actions of other hospital or office personnel working under her.

EXTENT OF INSURANCE PROTECTION. The malpractice insurance policy gives the insured two principal benefits. The typical malpractice insurance policy requires the insurance company to bear all costs of defending and representing the nurse including the cost of retaining an attorney to represent the nurse's side of the case. There is substantial cost in defending a nurse against a claim, even if it is totally groundless. In return, the policy usually provides that the insurance company will have the right to make the decisions in handling and defending against the claim. The basic provision of the malpractice insurance policy requires the insurance company to pay for all losses incurred by the nurse, including settlements made out of court, up to the face value of the policy. For example, a $5,000/$15,000 insurance policy obligates the insurance company in the amount of $5,000 per claim and $15,000 per policy year. If the nurse has this policy and a patient recovers a judgment for $10,000, the insurance company would have to pay the first $5,000 and the nurse would have to pay the remaining $5,000. If the insurance company has paid out $5,000 on two different claims during the year and another $10,000 judgment is issued that year against the nurse, the insurance company would pay $5,000 and the nurse would pay $5,000.

The insurance company usually retains the right to decide whether a claim will be defended or settled out of court. If the insurance company wants to settle a claim and the nurse insists that it be defended in court, the nurse may be obligated, under some malpractice insurance policies, to pay that amount of the judgment in excess of the amount for which the insurance company could have reached an out of court settlement. Therefore a nurse discussing the out of court settlement with her insurance company should be aware of her obligations under the insurance policy if she forces the case to be defended.

The nurse's insurance should provide coverage for all claims brought against her whether they are based upon her own actions or the actions of other persons for whom she is legally responsible.

How MUCH MALPRACTICE INSURANCE SHOULD THE NURSE CARRY? The nurse must decide for herself how much insurance she needs. She should have sufficient coverage so that the chances of her suffering a loss in excess of her coverage are so remote as not to be worth insuring against. Some insurance companies recommend low-limits policies, rationalizing that the increase in the amount of insurance purchased by doctors causes the judges and courts to award increasingly larger judgments to injured patients. Perhaps this is true, but the nurse found liable in the amount of $100,000 and whose policy has limits of $5,000 will be vexed by her own failure to obtain adequate insurance coverage. Furthermore the amount of a nurse's insurance is not permissible evidence to set before the jury, so that the nurse cannot inform the jury that she has only $5,000 in insurance.

The insurance company earns the malpractice insurance premium by the paper work involved in instituting a policy, by defending the nurse, and by paying claims. It is very likely that the costs of administering a malpractice insurance policy are greater for the administration of the policy and defending claims than for paying large claims. For this reason the premium on malpractice insurance does not increase substantially when the amount of coverage is increased. In many forms of insurance the premium rate is quoted as x number of dollars per thousand of coverage. For example, $10,000 worth of life insurance coverage usually costs ten times the amount of $1,000 worth of coverage. However with malpractice insurance there is only a relatively small increase in premium when coverage is increased. Many insurance companies selling this form of insurance are not particularly anxious to sell high-limits policies because they believe that the additional premium is not large enough to justify the large risks. For the nurse, the additional premium is well justified, especially when she considers the fact that malpractice insurance premiums are fully deductible business expenses. When we review the premiums charged for the various amounts of malpractice insurance for the nurse we find an approximate difference of $5.00 per year between the high-limits and the low-limits policy. It is recommended that the nurse undecided between two levels of malpractice insurance coverage should elect the higher coverage policy.

The smallest malpractice coverage and the largest contain the same provisions for defense of the nurse so nothing is gained in terms of defense when purchasing a high-limits policy. The added protection is for the situation in which the jury awards a large amount of money to an injured party. When a court or jury is considering the amount to award the injured patient, they consider sex, age, dependents, employment, future earning capacities, and financial loss to survivors or dependents. The jury is really putting a price tag on a life or on an injury, which is determined by the costs of rehabilitating the injured party and the remuneration for lost earnings.

PROPER USE OF MALPRACTICE INSURANCE. The malpractice insurance policy usually states that the nurse is required to cooperate with the insurance company in the defense of the claim. The nurse should notify her insurance company of any threatened claim at the earliest possible moment, and there is no need to wait until a lawsuit is actually filed against her. If the nurse has reason to believe that the patient intends to claim malpractice against her she should immediately notify her insurance company. She may have reason to suspect a claim when a patient makes an oral threat, or when she knows that the patient has been injured in such a manner and to such an extent as to readily suggest that a malpractice claim will follow against her.

Many doctors and nurses are reluctant to notify the insurance company of a malpractice threat unless there has been a lawsuit filed. This is a mistake. Time may be of the essence and the insurance company may be able to settle the claim quickly and for a smaller amount before the lawsuit is filed. The insurance company that believes that its chances of defending or settling a malpractice claim have been damaged because the doctor or nurse has failed to notify them of that threat may fall back on the clause in the policy releasing the company from any liability if they have not received timely notice of the threatened claim.

The nurse threatened with a malpractice lawsuit should refrain from any action that might be construed as admitting liability to the patient. Once her insurance company has been notified, she should not discuss the claim with the patient or his attorney; all inquiries should be referred to the insurance company. If the nurse is visited by an attorney or investigator representing the patient she should refuse to discuss the case with him. Even to the point of being impolite the nurse should refuse to meet with the attorney. She should immediately notify the insurance company or the attorney that the insurance company has provided and ask how they want her to proceed. If the patient returns to discuss the case, the nurse should ask the insurance company for guidance. Perhaps the discussion with the patient might be a way of avoiding the malpractice lawsuit, but it could result in making the case harder to defend. The insurance company should be consulted and their advice followed. The nurse should never under any circumstance discuss her insurance coverage with a patient or even admit that she has insurance; she should never name the insurer or indicate the extent to which she is insured. If a patient asks her about this she should ignore the question. This is a personal matter for the nurse and should not be open to discussion. The nurse who discusses her insurance coverage with a patient runs the risk that the company will deny coverage on this basis.

In the event that the insurance company denies coverage for one of the reasons discussed, the nurse must defend the claim and pay the settlements or judgments herself. She may then decide to bring suit against the insurance company to let a court decide whether the insurance company had ample grounds for denying coverage. This problem can be avoided if the nurse follows these simple rules concerning notifying the insurance company and not discussing insurance with her patient. Malpractice insurance is purchased for the protection it gives the nurse. The nurse should use it in the most efficient manner to insure that she will get the protection she has purchased.

MALPRACTICE INSURANCE AVAILABLE TO NURSES. Malpractice insurance is relatively inexpensive for nurses. Many insurance companies do not have a special malpractice policy for the nurse, but merely adapt a physicians and dentists policy or a general personal liability insurance policy to provide professional protection for the nurse. The following are some of the forms in which malpractice insurance is available to members of the nursing profession.

PROGRAM SPONSORED BY THE AMERICAN NURSES' ASSOCIATION. Registered nurses who are members of the American Nurses' Association are in the enviable position of being able to purchase malpractice insurance on a group basis. The American Nurses' Association sponsors and approves a Nurses' Liability Policy which is underwritten by the Globe Indemnity Company. A unique feature of the policy offered by the ANA and Globe is the incorporation of personal liability insurance with professional liability insurance. The personal liability feature provides protection against claims for bodily injury or property damage arising from personal (i.e., nonprofessional) acts. The policy excludes all forms of auto insurance coverage.

Practical nurses should contact their organizations to determine whether any form of group malpractice insurance is available to them. A practical nurse can be sued for malpractice so she has the same need for malpractice insurance as the registered nurse.

PROFESSIONAL LIABILITY POLICY. Many of the major insurance companies that write malpractice insurance adapt their "physicians and dentists" form to make it applicable to nurses. There is no reason to object to this since the policy is easily adapted. The nurse should carefully read this very short policy to make sure that it meets her needs.

GENERAL LIABILITY POLICY. The premium on a nurse's malpractice insurance policy is so low that many insurance agents are understandably reluctant to work with the nurse in providing her with malpractice coverage. The professional liability policy written on an individual basis is attractive to the insurance agent only when he believes this will be a basis on which he will get the nurse's other insurance business. To make the business attractive, many insurance companies will offer the nurse malpractice insurance as part of a general liability policy or as a part of an automobile-general liability policy. This policy will provide professional insurance, personal liability insurance, and automobile liability insurance. By combining the three forms of insurance coverage into one policy it becomes attractive for the insurance company to spend some time with the nurse in meeting her liability insurance needs. This form of coverage is attractive to the nurse because she gets three kinds of coverage in a single policy, paying a single premium each year, which simplifies her insurance program.

NURSES IN FEDERAL SERVICE. Nurses in military service or the nurse employed by the Veterans Administration or the U. S. Public Health Service are in an unusually protected situation. The Federal Tort Claims Act allows an injured patient to sue the federal government for the nurse's negligent actions, and it is assumed that in most instances the patient will elect to sue the government instead of the nurse. The armed services nurse has little exposure to malpractice claims from servicemen patients, since the recent court decisions hold that the serviceman has no right to sue a military officer when that officer acted in the course of his military duties, even if he was, in fact, negligent. Therefore, the nurse in military service or the nurse employed by the Veterans Administration or the U. S. Public Health Service has much less chance of being sued for malpractice and having to defend herself than does the civilian nurse.

Because of the reduced exposure to loss, some insurance companies have a special malpractice insurance policy for dentists and physicians in this category, which is usually available at a reduced premium. Because of the relatively low cost of malpractice insurance for nurses the insurance companies do not offer such special in-service policies. Although it is not likely that the nurse will be sued by a serviceman or his dependent, there is always the possibility. There is also the possibility that the case will fall within one of the exceptions to the Federal Tort Claims Act and that the dependent will not have the opportunity to sue the government, having recourse only against the nurse. Thus it is recommended that nurses maintain their malpractice insurance while in federal service.

Disability Insurance

Perhaps the most misunderstood form of insurance is disability insurance, also known as salary continuation insurance, accident and health insurance, accident and sickness insurance, and many other names. Disability insurance is perhaps the single most important insurance need of the nurse who relies upon her income from nursing to support herself and the members of her family.

Disability insurance provides a fixed income while the insured is unable to work due to sickness or accident, without regard to how the insured spends the money. It does not pay medical, surgical or hospital bills—it is a continuation of salary. The amount of disability income that the insured will receive depends upon the terms of the policy. Most disability insurance policies permit the purchaser to elect the amount of benefit she wishes to receive in the event of disability and the premium level depends on the benefit level. Rates also go up as the age of the policy holder increases, because the chances of becoming disabled increase with age. The rates are also slightly higher when the insured elects to pay the insurance premium on a monthly or quarterly basis rather than on an annual or semi-annual basis. The time to purchase disability insurance is when the nurse is healthy and able to work. When she is disabled it is too late to purchase the coverage. Most disability insurance policies provide that the applicant must submit a medical history and if there is evidence that the applicant is not healthy the policy will not be issued. In some instances the insurance companies will provide so-called waiver underwriting when the applicant has one specific health problem, meaning that the company will provide benefits for disability from all causes except this one stated health problem. Waiver underwriting is never implemented without the written consent of the insured.

GROUP AND INDIVIDUAL PROGRAMS.   Disability insurance programs are sponsored by many professional groups. The main advantage of the group policy, in addition to generally lower premiums, is that the individual usually gets non-cancellable protection if he remains in the group and the group policy stays in effect. Both the professional and the practical nurse should investigate the group disability insurance programs sponsored by their national and state organizations. The disability benefit may be found as an "extra" benefit in some life insurance programs such as the life insurance program sponsored by the American Nurses' Association.

BENEFITS. There are two essential elements that must be reviewed when comparing disability insurance programs. It is not sufficient to compare the premiums and select the lowest cost policy. The benefit period should also be reviewed for "waiting periods" and for length of benefits, as this has direct impact on the premiums.

The waiting period before disability benefits commence is second only to the amount of the monthly benefit in determining the cost of the insurance. A no-waiting period disability program usually means that the benefits start on the first day of disability due to an accident and the first day of hospitalization due to sickness. If the individual is not hospitalized due to the sickness the benefits will not start until the eighth day. The disability program that has a thirty day waiting period before benefits commence is considerably less expensive, since most disabilities do not go past thirty days. The nurse considering the selection of a disability program should consider her ability to go without an income for the first thirty days of a disability in determining whether she can risk the purchase of this less expensive form of coverage.

Most policies provide benefit periods of five years for total disability due to accident and two years for disability due to sickness. Extended benefits providing longer periods of coverage are available under most disability insurance programs at an increased premium.

Nurses employed by hospitals or physicians usually can assume that their salary will be continued for the first part of a disability due to the accumulation of sick leave or vacation time. This is an independent decision each nurse must make when determining whether she needs "first day" benefits or if she can accept the less expensive coverage which has a thirty day waiting period.

The claims form usually requires that the nurse submit a statement of her disability and a statement signed by her physician stating that she was disabled. Obviously the nurse will have to be disabled to receive benefits and the evidence submitted on her behalf will have to demonstrate this fact.

Benefits are payable on either a monthly or weekly basis depending on the policy and a nurse disabled for a portion of a payment period will receive proportionate benefits. Therefore there is no real difference between programs stating that benefits are paid weekly or monthly. Because disability benefits are a substitute for income they are paid directly to the insured nurse, who may then use this money to pay medical and hospital bills or for any other purpose, since this is the same money as her usual personal income.

EXCLUSIONS.   Disability policies commonly have the same exclusions. An exclusion means that benefits are not payable if the disability results from one of the excluded risks. The most common exclusion is disability due to pregnancy. Other exclusions usually found in these policies are for suicide or self destruction or any attempt thereat, war, and flying as a crew member or as a pilot.

ACCIDENTAL DEATH AND DISMEMBERMENT.   Some disability insurance programs contain accidental death and dismemberment benefits which tend to confuse the primary purpose of the insurance. The accidental death benefit in some disability programs provides a fixed life insurance benefit in the event that death results from an accident. In this way the insurance company pays the beneficiary some of the benefits they would have paid if the insured were disabled. To some degree it removes the bad effect that would otherwise exist when the insurance company would have a financial benefit if the insured dies rather than is disabled. The accidental death benefit is clearly not a substitute for a life insurance program. It is a relatively small amount of life insurance and does not pay any benefits if the cause of death is something other than an accident.

The dismemberment benefit is even more confusing. Many disability policies show a stated amount payable if the insured suffers the loss (dismemberment) of a finger, eye, arm, leg, or any combination of these. In this case loss of an eye would mean loss of use of an eye or eyes. Under the accidental dismemberment benefit the insured who has suffered this loss would have the option of electing the cash amount stated for the dismemberment or to take the monthly amount of disability benefits. The election will naturally be based upon the disabling effect of the dismemberment. For example, the nurse who has lost both hands and is disabled for life would obviously be better off taking the monthly disability benefit rather than a lump sum for the dismemberment. Sometimes the insured does not realize that the dismemberment benefit is an alternative to the monthly disability benefit and not in addition to this benefit.

Some policies offer surgical benefits on an optional basis. According to a fee schedule, the participating nurse who elects this optional coverage will receive a fixed number of dollars for each surgical procedure she suffers. This is a very limited benefit and the nurse who elects this surgical benefit should be aware of its limitations. For example, the surgical benefit may be stated as one fixed sum but this is usually the maximum amount that will be paid and not the amount that will be paid in all instances. Compare this to the monthly benefit under the disability portion of the policy, which is the exact amount the nurse will receive if she is disabled.

DISABILITY INSURANCE AS A FRINGE BENEFIT. Disability insurance is an ideal fringe benefit for a doctor or hospital to provide for the employed nurse. The application of the insurance relieves the hospital and doctor from the moral question of how long to continue the salary of a disabled nurse. The tax aspect of disability insurance also makes this a desirable fringe benefit. If the nurse purchases the insurance for herself she does it with post-tax dollars and the purchase is not tax deductible. If the doctor or other employer purchases the insurance for the nurse the cost is a deductible business expense. For example, the nurse receives one dollar in salary from which she pays 18¢ in taxes. She has 82¢ with which to purchase the insurance. If the doctor purchases the insurance as a fringe benefit he has the full dollar to spend on insurance and the nurse gets the whole dollar's worth of insurance. If the doctor considers the difference between spending one dollar on a fringe benefit or one dollar on salary there is no difference to him because both dollars are fully deductible business expenses. The difference to the nurse is getting one dollar or 82¢ worth of insurance.

DISABILITY INSURANCE AND RETIREMENT. The nurse should not confuse disability insurance with her retirement needs. Disability insurance is used when the individual is unable to work due to accident or sickness and not to provide a retirement income. Because of the tendancy of older persons to use disability insurance as a form of retirement program most disability insurance policies, whether they are individual or group, will not provide coverage past age 60 or 65.

Hospital Money Plan

The ability of the insurance industry to continually find new methods for packaging insurance is unquestioned. A recent development is the Hospital Money Plan which falls somewhere between disability insurance and medical, surgical and hospital insurance. Disability insurance pays benefits without regard to whether or not you are hospitalized. Hospitalization insurance pays either all or a part of hospital costs. A Hospital Money Plan pays a daily benefit while you are hospitalized, and this benefit can be used for any purpose. A Hospital Money Plan can be looked upon as a special form of disability insurance, paying benefits only when the insured is hospitalized. Because the Hospital Money Plan does not pay benefits for all disabilities (only for those resulting in hospitalization), and because it does not pay total hospital bills, it is less expensive than disability insurance or hospitalization insurance.

Medical, Surgical, and Hospital Insurance

Medical, surgical, and hospital policies reimburse the insured for these expenses when incurred by the insured on behalf of herself or her family. These policies can be purchased on an individual or group basis.

The medical, surgical, and hospital insurance may be purchased through Blue Shield or Blue Cross, or from any number of commercial insurance companies that sell this form of insurance. It is possible to separate hospital insurance from medical and surgical insurance and purchase one without the other, although they are usually purchased together.

Some policies provide for the insurance company to pay the loss to the insured, who in turn will pay her own surgical or hospital bill. More commonly the insurance company makes the payment directly to the hospital or physician, who then bills the patient for the difference between the amount of the bill and the amount received from the insurance company.

Many nurses find that a hospital-surgical plan coupled with an accident and sickness plan give them a good basic insurance program to protect them while they are ill. The accident and sickness program restores part of the nurse's income while she is unable to work, and the hospital-surgical plan pays her medical and hospital bills arising from the disability.

Major Medical

Major medical insurance provides coverage for the catastrophic medical expenses that may be in excess of the insurance provided by the normal medical, surgical, and hospital expense policies. The usual major medical provides for co-insurance, i.e., after the basic amount is paid by the insurance company, the insured must participate by paying a percentage (perhaps 20 per cent) of all additional medical expenses, with the insurance company paying the remainder. The policy is usually, but not necessarily, sold in conjunction with medical, surgical, and hospital insurance.

Unemployment Insurance

Although the nurse may not consider "unemployment insurance" as really being insurance, the state and federal unemployment insurance funds do operate as insurance funds. The nurse considering her insurance needs and coverage does not readily consider unemployment insurance because there is little need to do so. If she is "covered" then she has no choice, she must participate in the unemployment insurance program as an employee whether she wants to or not. The doctor, as an employer, has little to do in the field of unemployment insurance other than to determine whether or not he is covered, and pay his taxes if covered.

The unemployment insurance concept is really one of industrial unemployment to protect the employee, who, through no fault of his own, is faced with unemployment caused by changes in industry. For this reason the unemployment insurance program is aimed at employers of large numbers of workers who may be subject to periods of unemployment.

The basis of the unemployment insurance program is the Federal Unemployment Tax Act, which imposes a payroll tax of 3% of the first $3,000 of wages paid to each employee by an employer who has four or more covered workers for some part of a day in each of 20 weeks during the calendar year. The Federal Unemployment Tax Act provides a credit system whereby the employer is given a credit against this tax for amounts which he has paid into a state unemployment insurance fund. The federal law was obviously a method for inducing the states to create insurance programs for the unemployed.

The crucial test to determine whether or not an employer is subject to this tax is the four employees test. If the doctor employs four or more persons for more than 20 weeks during the year, even if the workers are employed on a part time basis, the doctor's practice becomes subject to the unemployment tax. This basis of four workers, which establishes responsibility for the tax, is contrasted to the workmen's compensation system whereby each state determines the minimum number of employees necessary for the employer to become subject to the state workmen's compensation law.

Only a few states impose a levy on the employees so that they have to contribute to the unemployment insurance fund. Benefits received by an unemployed nurse pursuant to the state unemployment insurance program are not subject to federal income taxes as earned income. Because of the demand for nurses, which results from the shortage of trained persons, it is not likely that a registered or a practical nurse will retain her eligibility for unemployment compensation for more than a few days.

Life Insurance

A nurse's life insurance program is a personal matter that does not necessarily have any bearing on the business, legal, and economic aspects of nursing. A short discussion of life insurance has been included because the nurse should have a basic understanding of the different kinds of life insurance, and because she should consider consulting the same insurance broker for advice on life insurance as she does for her professional insurance.

The only limit on the different kinds of life insurance policies available is the ingenuity of competing life insurance companies. All the special policies and "new" policies are merely variations on the basic types of life insurance, altered to fit a special individual or class of individuals. The basic types of life insurance should be reviewed by the nurse to determine which best meets her need.

Ordinary life is the oldest and most common form of life insurance sometimes referred to as "whole life" or "regular life." Under the terms of the ordinary life insurance policy, the insured must pay a fixed premium annually, or at more frequent intervals throughout his life, and the beneficiary is entitled to receive the full face value of the policy only upon the death of the insured.

Limited-pay life policies are the same as ordinary life insofar as they are payable to the beneficiary only upon the death of the insured. Limited-pay life differs from ordinary life in that the insured makes premium payments only for a specified number of years, provided that the insured lives for that period. Naturally, the annual payments would be higher for the same individual for limited-pay life as opposed to ordinary life, as the insured will be making premium payments for fewer years.

Term insurance covers the insured and makes payment only if the insured dies within the term. A nurse with a five-year term policy makes her premium payments during that given-year period. If she dies within the period, the beneficiary collects the face amount of the policy. If she dies after the term the beneficiary gets nothing. As might be expected, term insurance has a lower annual premium than either ordinary or limited-pay life insurance.

An ordinary or limited-pay life policy will usually have some cash value while term insurance will usually have none. Because the term policy is in force for a specified number of years, it automatically terminates at the end of the term unless renewed. The ordinary life and limited-pay life give the insured an opportunity at any time to cash in the policy. When the policy is cashed in, the insurance company returns a portion of the premium to the insured in return for being released from obligations to pay anything to the beneficiary upon the death of the insured. If the insured cashes in the policy she gets some of her premium back and ends the contract of life insurance with the insurance company. An alternative to cashing the policy for the insured who will not make further premium payments is to use the cash value to purchase paid up insurance. The cash value will be used to buy an appreciably smaller policy which will give the beneficiary some benefits upon the death of the insured without any further premium payment by the insured.

Because the term policy usually has no cash value and presents no possibility for dividends, it is usually the least expensive form of insurance. It is especially recommended for the individual who needs a large amount of insurance while she is still unable to make large premium payments. It is especially suited to the nurse who presently has family obligations and little income available for insurance.

A participating policy gives the insured the right to participate in the dividends enjoyed by the insurance company due to a favorable mortality rate. These dividends can be accumulated and used to pay future premiums. Nonparticipating policies do not carry dividends, and are usually sold at lower premium rates than participating policies.

THE AMERICAN NURSES' ASSOCIATION GROUP LIFE INSURANCE PROGRAM. The American Nurses' Association and the state nurses' associations are in a particularly advantageous position for the purchase of group insurance. Under a group policy a group of individuals contribute their premium dollars in payment for protection for the group. The standardization of the policy and the administration of the policies issued to the members of the group make it possible for the insurance company to effectively reduce the premium for a large group. Membership in the group, in this case membership in the American Nurses' Association or in the state nurses' associations, is a prerequisite to participation in the group policy.

With one exception, the American Nurses' Association group life insurance policy can be characterized as a fixed premium, variable life insurance benefit program, which means that the annual premium does not increase each year, but the amount payable on the death of the insured depends on the age of the insured at the time of death. The exception is that the annual premium for the nurse under age 35 is somewhat reduced. The premium level is the same for all participating nurses ages 35 to 70. At ages below 45 the face value of the policy is $6000 and this is reduced to $5000 at age 45 to 50, $3000 from 50 to 55, $2000 from 55 to 60, $1500 from 60 to 65 and then $1000 to age 70. After age 70 members are eligible only for $500 coverage at an increased premium. The premiums for the nurse under age 35 are $20 per year and then the premium level remains at $30 per year until age 70. It can be expected that there will be periodic changes in the premium and benefit level, since the experience of the group life insurance company warrants some changes. This is a very attractive life insurance policy offering maximum coverage for a small amount of money. Whether or not this will be a sufficient amount of life insurance coverage for the nurse depends upon her particular needs and especially upon whether or not other persons are dependent upon her for their financial support. The ANA policy is a term policy so there is no cash value, no paid up value, and no dividends. It is simple life insurance providing the maximum amount of coverage for the least number of dollars.

The group life insurance program offered by the American Nurses' Association and underwritten by the Prudential Insurance Company of America offers an additional accidental death benefit in the same amount as the regular life insurance coverage. If the nurse is 47 years old and has $5,000 coverage, her beneficiaries will receive $5,000 if she dies from natural causes and $10,000 if she dies from accidental causes. The ANA-Prudential program also includes a small monthly disability income benefit for those nurses who become disabled prior to age 60. If the nurse has been disabled for more than nine months and has been a participant in the life insurance program for more than one year, she becomes eligible to receive $50 per month as a disability income benefit. Monthly disability benefits are payable to the nurse who is totally disabled for up to 50 months, but not past age 60. This disability benefit is rather meager but it is not the basis of the whole policy; it is a small extra added to the life insurance policy.

Tax Aspects of Insurance

In the purchase of both personal and professional insurance one cannot ignore the tax aspects of the deduction of the premiums and the tax on the benefits. The following is a review of various insurance coverages with specific attention to the tax aspects of the coverage. (For a more detailed analysis of the nurse's tax responsibilities see the chapter on federal income taxation.)

Professional Liability Insurance

Premiums paid for professional liability insurance are considered ordinary and necessary business expenses and are deductible for federal income tax purposes.

Accident and Sickness Insurance

Accident and sickness insurance provides benefits to an individual who is disabled and cannot earn his living from his usual sources. If an individual purchases this insurance for himself, the premiums are not usually tax deductible. Although a few courts have said that the premiums are either partially or fully deductible, the Internal Revenue Service has consistently maintained that no deduction will be allowed for premiums paid by an individual for his own accident and sickness insurance coverage.

If an employer provides accident and sickness insurance for his employee as a fringe benefit, the employer can deduct the costs of the insurance as a business expense.

Benefits received under an accident and sickness program are taxfree. An individual who earns $100 per week and has $100 per week insurance protection actually gets an increase in her earnings when she is disabled and receives benefits under this insurance program. The $100 she is receiving as earnings is subject to tax, but when she is disabled the $100 she receives is taxfree. For this reason most insurance companies that provide accident and sickness insurance coverage will not provide for insurance in excess of 80 per cent of the customary earnings of the individual. To do otherwise would be to make it too advantageous for the policyholder to become disabled through accident or sickness.

Accident and sickness insurance does not provide for payments for hospital, medical, or surgical fees. It provides income when disabled without regard to hospital, medical, or surgical costs. When some amount of hospital, medical, or surgical insurance is included in the accident and sickness insurance program, that part of the premium allocated to these additional coverages is tax-deductible.

Medical, Surgical, and Hospital Insurance

Premiums paid by an individual for her own hospital, medical, and surgical insurance are deductible just as though they were regular medical expenses. The premiums are added to the other medical expenses for the year to determine whether the individual's medical expenses were in excess of three per cent of her gross income. The amount in excess of three per cent is deductible. This changes when the individual reaches age 65 and the total medical expenses are deductible.

Medical, surgical, and hospital insurance reimburses the policyholder for payments which he has made to physicians, surgeons, and hospitals. Sometimes the payments are made directly to the doctor or hospital. To the extent that the insurance provides for payment of these medical bills the individual cannot deduct these expenses as medical expenses. If he pays a portion of the medical expenses, this portion is deductible in addition to the premiums which he has paid for this insurance.

Medical, surgical, and hospital insurance, whether provided by Blue Cross and Blue Shield or by commercial insurance companies, has become a fringe benefit because the employer takes the full deduction for premiums he pays on behalf of the employee. Naturally, if the employer pays the premium, the employee cannot deduct the costs of the premium as a medical expense.

Benefits received under hospital, surgical, and medical insurance are not taxable to the beneficiary.

Major Medical Insurance

Major medical insurance is treated the same as hospital, medical, and surgical insurance. The premiums are deductible as medical expenses and the benefits are not taxable.

Life Insurance

Premiums paid by an individual for life insurance on her own life are not deductible from federal income taxation. If the beneficiary of the life insurance policy is a named individual, the beneficiary does not have to pay income tax on the proceeds of the policy.

If the beneficiary of the life insurance policy is the estate of the insured, the proceeds of the policy become a part of the estate and thus subject to state and federal estate taxes. For this reason, it is common for a man to name his wife or family as the beneficiary of his life insurance rather than his estate.

If a corporation purchases life insurance on the life of an employee, that employee can receive up to $50,000 worth of life insurance without any taxation. The premiums paid by an employer for life insurance of an employee as a fringe benefit are deductible business expenses for the employer. The employee pays taxes on that portion of the premium which goes for all life insurance in excess of $50,000. When this amount is exceeded, the amount of additional premium is considered income to the employee and he pays taxes on this income. The $50,000 is not subject to taxation when the beneficiary of the employee is a named individual.

This means that the doctor can deduct as a business expense the cost of providing life insurance for his employees as a fringe benefit, but he cannot deduct the cost of providing life insurance for himself. His own life insurance costs are considered to be a personal and not a business expense.

Since the premiums for an employees' insurance policy are tax-deductible by an employer, there is an incentive for the employer and employee to agree to take this fringe benefit in lieu of a salary increase. The employer achieves no particular benefit from this because the salary and the insurance are both deductible business expenses. The employee benefits because he gets the insurance premium paid with pretax dollars.

For example, the employee is in the 18 per cent tax bracket and gets a $100 raise. The employee has $82 to use for insurance. The other $18 went for taxes. If the employer purchases the insurance for the employee, the whole $100 could be used for the purchase of insurance.

Retirement Programs

The nurse who is dependent upon her income from her profession as her sole means of support cannot think of her retirement program too early in her career. The facts of economic life are such that a wage earner can no longer plan on saving a portion of her income so that she will have ample funds for retirement years. Our society has become so sophisticated that such a simple savings device can result in financial disaster.

Rather than merely saving for retirement, the nurse should have a retirement program that will anticipate present and future earning capacity and financial needs, balancing savings with needs, so that the nurse will be protected in her old age. The need for such a program is obvious when one considers the fact that the value of the dollar has been steadily decreasing. Gradual inflation, which has become a normal part of our economy, has its worst effect on the person living on a fixed retirement income, especially when the amount of the income was fixed long before retirement. It is also clear that bank interest earned on savings is not sufficient to keep up with the gradual decrease in the value of the dollar and the rise in prices.

The retirement problems of the self-employed nurse, the nurse employed by one or more doctors, and the nurse employed by a hospital are different and will be considered separately.

The Self-Employed Nurse

The self-employed nurse, defined here as a special duty nurse or a nurse who changes employers so often as not to qualify for any employer-sponsored retirement program, is the nurse with the greatest retirement problem. Since she does not have a retirement program the main sources of income in her retirement years are social security and personal savings. Social security benefits constitute a substantial part of her retirement income. She can elect to receive benefits at age 60, 62, or 65, and the longer she puts off receiving these benefits the higher her monthly benefit will be. But social security benefits, even with periodic increases, must be supplemented with other funds. Savings funds are better than nothing, but they are the least economical way for the nurse to provide for her old age. The main fault with savings funds is that they do not keep pace with the depreciation of the dollar. Although stock market investments are one established method for maintaining the value of savings many nurses hesitate to "play the market" for fear that they cannot afford the risk the market always presents. The complexity of stock market investing also keeps most nurses away, perhaps only for the reason that they cannot give enough time to serious study of stocks and the stock market.

BONDS. United States Savings Bonds and other bonds provide a fixed interest rate on investment funds but they provide such a generally low rate of interest that they cannot be considered as any better than earning bank interest for retirement purposes. Bonds present more security than stocks but they also provide less earnings.

THE MUTUAL FUND. The mutual fund, a lumping together of the investments of many people to spread the risk and share the profits of investments, has become an important part of retirement programs. An individual can purchase shares in a mutual fund in the same way that shares of a corporation are purchased. The mutual fund uses its money to purchase stocks for its participating members, presenting two major benefits for the novice investor: expertise in selecting stocks and diversification. The mutual fund has enough money to invest that it can realistically purchase many different stocks and have sufficient diversification so that bad results in one stock will be offset by good results in another. The general performance of mutual stocks is often less spectacular than other means of investment, but the risks are much less because of the diversification. A mutual fund, whereby the nurse contributes a fixed number of dollars to the fund each month, presents a very simple means for establishing a retirement program that will keep pace with depreciation of the dollar and creeping inflation.

There are so-called "load" and "no-load" mutual funds. A load mutual fund is one that takes a certain percentage of the investment as a fee as soon as the money is invested. For example, an 8.5% front-end load mutual fund would take 8.5¢ on each investment dollar as an entry fee. Some of the large mutual funds have this front-end load. Others are called rear-end load because at the time the money is taken out of the fund there is a percentage charge. There are also some very good no-load funds. The investment results of the no-load and the 8.5% load funds are not different so it is generally unwise to invest in the load fund. Most people who invest in a load fund do not realize that there are no-load funds. Any good stockbroker will be willing to tell the nurse the names of good no-load mutual funds. Most if not all mutual funds will have a ½% annual service charge to cover the costs of administering the fund.

The major disadvantage of the mutual fund is that at retirement the nurse does not know how much of her funds she can spend each year, since she does not know how long she will live. For example, the nurse retires at age 60 and has $50,000 in savings and mutual funds. Should she spend $5,000 per year and anticipate that she will live for ten years, or should she spend $2,500 per year in anticipation of living to age 80? On one hand she may use all her savings prematurely and on the other hand she may live on a meager allowance and die with all her funds intact. For this reason some people elect annuities to provide them with a monthly income for life.

ANNUITIES. An annuity issued by a life insurance company can be purchased while the individual is working or at retirement time. In its simplest form an annuity provides a monthly income for life. Some annuities are guaranteed for a stated number of years so that if the individual dies soon after purchasing the annuity a portion of the monies invested in the annuity will be paid to the beneficiary. The nurse in the hypothetical case who has $50,000 at retirement at age 60 would be in an ideal position to purchase an annuity. This means that the $50,000 or a portion thereof, would be paid to the life insurance company in return for a monthly income for life. In this way the nurse would guarantee that she does not use her retirement funds too fast or too slowly.

A nurse can purchase either a fixed or a variable annuity. A fixed annuity provides a fixed monthly income at retirement and the variable annuity provides a monthly income which will vary depending on the performance of the stock market. The variable annuity is analogous to a mutual fund inasmuch as the funds are invested in the stock market and the value of the annuity will depend on stock market performance.

The annuity can be purchased long before retirement as an alternative to a mutual fund. A life insurance company will issue an annuity based upon the contribution of so many dollars per year during the nurse's working years, and will then pay her an annuity at the time she retires.

SELF-EMPLOYED INDIVIDUALS TAX RETIREMENT ACT OF 1962. One of the tax problems in providing for retirement income is that the retirement funds are usually invested after federal income taxes. For example, the nurse earns $100 which she wishes to invest for her retirement. As a self-employed individual she first pays the taxes on this $100 which may leave her with only $80 for retirement investment. Contrast this to many corporate employees who can invest the whole $100 without taxes until retirement. The benefit to the corporate employee is that the tax at retirement will probably be at a lower rate than during employment years and the earnings on the retirement fund will not be taxed until retirement. The corporate employee's retirement funds will build up faster because the funds that would otherwise go into taxes are earning interest. This was a

gross discrimination against the self-employed, so in 1962 Congress enacted the Self-Employed Individuals Tax Retirement Act, which was
amended in 1966, and is often called the Keogh Act.

Effective 1968 a self-employed individual can contribute as much as
the lesser of $2,500 or 10 per cent of his net earnings per year to his
qualified retirement program without paying taxes on this money. In
effect, the amount of the contribution to the individual's retirement program is a tax deduction for that year. At retirement these funds become
taxable. There is a clear tax savings under the retirement plans that
qualify under this act.

A self-employed nurse should discuss with her bank or insurance
company the possibilities of creating a retirement program which would
qualify for this favorable tax treatment under the Keogh Act. This alternative exists only for the self-employed nurse, but as will be seen later in
this chapter, the benefits under the Keogh Act for the nurse employed by
a doctor are even greater.

The Nurse Employed by a Doctor

A long term employee of a doctor or group of doctors should discuss
with her employer the creation of a retirement program. The doctor may
find it feasible to create a retirement program for himself and his employees
that will provide some measure of retirement security for all of them. In
this sense an employer-paid retirement program is no different than any
other fringe benefit which a nurse.may receive as a condition of her
employment.

If the doctor creates a retirement program for the nurse the doctor's
contributions to the retirement program will or will not be taxable to the
nurse in the year that the contributions are made, depending upon whether
the contributions are made under the Keogh Act or to another qualified
retirement program. The nurse's own contributions to the program will
be made after taxes.

The Self-Employed Individuals Tax Retirement Act of 1962 was the
result of joint efforts of many groups of self-employed persons to remove
the discrimination in taxing retirement programs. Many eligible persons
are just becoming aware of the tax savings features of this law and the
valuable benefits which are available.

One of the most important provisions of the Keogh Act is that the
doctor must contribute the same percentage of funds to his employees retirement program as he does to his own fund. These funds may not be
deducted from wages of the employee and ostensibly may not be a
substitute for salary increases that might otherwise be paid to the

employee. A doctor may make a tax deductible contribution of up to ten per cent of his annual income to his retirement program but not to exceed $2,500 in any one year. He must himself contribute the same percentage of the nurse's salary to her retirement fund.

The money placed in the nurse's retirement plan belongs to her and she does not pay any taxes on it until retirement. However the funds belong to her under any circumstances, including death or discontinuation of employment. Any time after the employment terminates the employee can take these funds out of the retirement program and she then pays only capital gains tax. The contribution is all the doctor's money so there is no way the Keogh Act can provide anything but additional income for employees of participating doctors. The significant fact is that the benefits of the Keogh Act are so attractive to the doctor that the cost of providing retirement benefits for his employees do not often deter the doctor from starting a Keogh Act retirement program. The funds which are in the nurse's Keogh Act retirement fund are earning interest which is not taxable to the nurse until she otherwise withdraws these funds from the retirement account. This is a tax savings which is even more attractive than the fact that the initial contribution to the fund is not taxable. The Keogh Act provides that the doctor may make additional contributions to the retirement fund not to exceed another ten per cent of income if he permits his employees to make similar voluntary contributions. These additional contributions are made by the doctor and nurse from post-tax dollars so there is no tax savings there. The tax savings for the additional contributions are in the fact that the earnings of these funds are not taxable until retirement or until the funds are withdrawn from the retirement program. The nurse who is pleased with the Keogh Act retirement fund may wish to give serious consideration to adding voluntary contributions to the fund, which will increase the total amount she receives at retirement.

Not all employees are entitled to these benefits under the Keogh Act. The law requires contributions only on behalf of those full time employees who have been in the doctor's employ for more than three years. However, the doctor can add short-term employees to the plan if he so wishes. One of the side benefits of the Keogh Act is that it becomes more attractive for a nurse to maintain her employment with one doctor rather than make periodic changes in employment.

The Nurse Employed by a Hospital

The Keogh Act applies only to nurses employed by self-employed doctors. However, there are many equally attractive retirement programs which are sponsored by nonprofit corporations, including hospitals, for their employees. The hospital does not have the same incentive for creating a retirement program as the doctor, but most hospitals nevertheless have retirement programs for their employees.

The hospital retirement program for its employees typically provides a joint contribution plan whereby the hospital and the nurse each contribute to the nurse's retirement program. The hospital contributions are not taxable to the nurse until she takes the funds out of the retirement plan and she makes her own contribution with post-tax dollars. The earnings of these retirement funds are also non-taxable until the year of distribution. Once the funds are placed in the retirement program they become vested in the nurse so that she never loses them. Hospitals as non-profit corporations are in a good position to provide well planned retirement programs for their employees.

Insurance Checklist for the Nurse

1. Malpractice Insurance: To protect against claims of malpractice arising out of nursing practice.

2. Life Insurance: To protect family and creditors.

3. Disability Insurance: To provide the nurse with an income while disabled due to accident or sickness.

4. Medical, Surgical, and Hospital Insurance: To provide funds for paying medical, surgical, and hospital bills for services rendered to the nurse or her family.

5. Major Medical: Insurance to afford added protection when the medical, surgical, and hospital insurance is inadequate to meet substantial needs.

6. Hospital Money Plan: To provide an income while hospitalized.

7. Unemployment Insurance.

8. Automobile Insurance: To protect the investment in an automobile and to protect against liability which may occur from using the automobile.

9. Theft Insurance: To protect against losses due to theft.

10. Retirement Plan: To provide a retirement income.

20   *Federal Income Taxation*

The Internal Revenue Service announces each year that many taxpayers who are unfamiliar with their obligations under the tax laws fail to take the proper deductions or fail to file in the manner that will result in the least taxation. There is nothing illegal or immoral in taking advantage of all deductions available and in preparing an income tax form in the way that produces the least amount of taxes as long as the law is not violated in the process. This chapter will discuss the various methods available to the nurse preparing her own tax return and then explore special deductions available to her.

Selection of Method of Filing

JOINT RETURN.   If the nurse is married and both spouses have an income, the joint return should be used. The filing of separate returns will rarely produce less total tax than the filing of a joint return. If the nurse is married at the end of the year she will be considered to have been married for the entire year for tax purposes. If the nurse is divorced at the end of the year she is considered to have been single for the entire year and cannot file a joint return. If the nurse is widowed during the year she is considered married for the year and can file a joint return for that year.

UNMARRIED HEAD OF HOUSEHOLD.   During the past few years the tax laws have been amended to remove some of the discrimination against the unmarried person who is providing a home for dependents. The nurse who can qualify as the unmarried head of a household will find that this results in a substantial reduction in her tax costs. To qualify for this category the nurse must either be unmarried or married to a nonresident alien. In addition, she must pay over half the cost of maintaining the residence of an unmarried child or any other person for whom she is entitled to a deduction for an exemption.

SHORT FORM. An individual who earns less than $10,000 per year and has less than $200 total of other wages, interests, and dividends, can use the short form, 1040A. This is a less complicated means for filing a tax return but it could be a costly venture depending upon the deductions to which the nurse is entitled. By using the short form the taxpayer takes a standard deduction and waives all rights to specific deductions. It is suggested that the nurse prepare her tax return in both the long and short forms and then submit the one that results in the smallest total tax.

LONG FORM. The fact that the nurse elects to use the long form does not preclude her from electing to using the standard deduction. This may be preferable under certain circumstances to using the short form, as some deductions are allowed in addition to the standard personal deduction.

Tax Myths

There are certain tax myths that appear to be rampant and should quickly be dispelled. Their existence illustrates a general lack of understanding of the federal income tax.

HIGHER TAX BRACKET. Sometimes one hears it said that "I did not want to earn that extra dollar because it placed me in a higher tax bracket," the idea here being that the earning of one extra dollar places the taxpayer in a higher tax bracket, resulting in a net loss. Generally, this is illogical. When the taxpayer's earnings place him in a higher tax bracket it does not mean that all his earnings are taxed at the higher rate, but only the additional earnings. For example, in the most extreme case, if an individual earns the extra dollar so that he is now in the 90% tax bracket, whereas before earning the extra dollar he was in the 87% tax bracket, this does not mean that this person's entire income is taxed at the 90% rate instead of the 87% rate, it just means that the last dollar is taxed at the higher rate. The extra dollar may only result in 10¢ net income after taxes but it certainly does not result in a net loss. It might be added parenthetically that this taxpayer is not paying 87% of his income in taxes, because each portion of his income is taxed at a different rate and it is doubtful that he is paying more than 50% of his total income in taxes.

There is only one circumstance in which the additional dollar of income might be costly, and that is when the individual earns less than $5,000, takes the standard deduction, and uses the tax table. Here it is conceivable that one dollar in additional earning can result in two or three dollars additional taxes. For example, under the 1967 tax table a single individual with earnings between $4,750 and $4,800 would pay $633 in taxes. An individual who earns $4,801 would pay $641 in taxes. Here the extra dollar that increased total taxable income from $4,800 to $4,801 would result in $7 in additional taxes. It is suggested that the mathematical chances of being in this situation are so remote that the nurse should not be preoccupied with this problem.

WHAT DID YOU GET BACK? Too often an individual judges his total tax obligation by what he had to pay (or got back) at the end of the year. The fact that an individual has to pay something extra at the end of the year, or that he gets something back, means that the amount withheld from wages was either too small or too great. This is not an accurate yardstick by which to judge whether or not you have prepared the best possible tax return to minimize taxes. If the nurse finds that she habitually has to pay additional funds at the end of the year she should reduce her personal exemptions so that additional funds are withheld from her paycheck. For example, a nurse who is entitled to claim herself and her mother as exemptions, and finds that she must make additional payments each year might consider only claiming one (instead of two) exemptions so that additional funds are withheld each payday. Perhaps the nurse might wish to consider claiming no exemptions so that more funds will be withheld and she will be guaranteed a refund each year, giving herself a very effective savings program. The fact that the nurse fails to claim all her exemptions for withholding purposes does not prevent her from claiming these exemptions when she files her tax return at the end of the year. Although an individual can claim fewer exemptions for withholding tax purposes than those to which she is entitled, the law will not permit her to claim additional exemptions.

Nurses who are self-employed are legally responsible for withholding funds from their own earnings and making periodic payments to the Internal Revenue Service. Nurses who are self-employed should call the local office of the Internal Revenue Service and request the booklet describing the withholding responsibilities of the self-employed individual.

Deductible and Nondeductible Expenses

AUTOMOBILE EXPENSES. Deductions are allowed for the expenses of operating an automobile when such expenditures are necessary to the nurse's professional duties. This does not include expenses of commuting between office, hospital, or home, since this has been determined to be "personal" expense. Examples of automobile expenses that may be considered business expenses are: attending professional society meetings, attending educational programs (if the educational program meets the tests discussed hereafter under the heading of Educational Expenses, driving patients to hospitals, commuting from the hospital to other hospitals, and necessary visits to laboratories and suppliers.

Since 1964 there has been a simple formula for computing the amount of the deduction allowed for the business expense of operating an automobile. The Internal Revenue Service has set a standard mileage rate of ten cents a mile for the first 15,000 miles of business use and seven cents a mile for each succeeding mile of business use. This standard mileage rate may be used in lieu of determining actual expenses. The rate for the first 15,000 miles is applied whether this involves the use of one or more automobiles. The nurse must maintain adequate records to establish the actual number of miles that her car was driven for business. Parking fees and tolls incurred during business use are deductible in addition to the standard mileage rate.

The deduction for automobile expenses may be taken by the alternate method of computing the total mileage driven during the year and the percentage driven for "business." This ratio can then be applied to the total expenses of the car for the year, including depreciation. It is probable that most nurses will find the standard mileage rate to be more feasible and having the best tax advantage.

EDUCATIONAL EXPENSES. Educational expenses are deductible as ordinary and necessary business expenses when the educational activity is undertaken primarily to maintain or improve existing skills, as opposed to acquiring new skills. Deduction is allowed for tuition, fees, and travel expenses. In general, the Internal Revenue Service still looks at the educational expense in terms of whether it is "customary" for nurses similarly situated, allowing the deduction if it is a customary expense.

A nurse taking a course of study in order to become a specialist cannot deduct the costs of education because her purpose is not to improve or maintain her present general skills. This situation can be contrasted with that of a nurse who takes a two week course in some specialty fields for the purpose of carrying on general nursing practice. In the latter case, the nurse's expenses for education are deductible because they were undertaken primarily to improve skills required of her in her profession.

The costs of attending a short-term course or clinical program are clearly deductible, and the only courses that probably are not deductible are those which lead to specialty practice or new professions. The federal courts have stated that educational expenses to obtain a nursing education are not deductible.

Generally, expenditures for travel, meals, and lodging while away from home overnight in pursuit of educational activities may be claimed as educational expenses in addition to tuition or fees for attending the educational program.

EXPENSES OF ATTENDING MEETINGS. The expenses of attending meetings of professional organizations are generally deductible as ordinary and necessary expenses of the profession. The deduction includes travel, meals, and lodging expenses in addition to the costs of registration.

DUES AND SUBSCRIPTIONS TO PROFESSIONAL SOCIETIES. A nurse may deduct the total expense of her dues to nurses' societies, including dues to specialty societies and study clubs. Subscriptions to official journals of nurses' societies are deductible, as are subscriptions to commercial publications of a professional nature. Subscriptions to other scientific publications of interest to the nurse in the practice of her profession are also deductible.

LICENSE EXAMINATION AND RENEWAL FEES. The fee sent to the state board of nursing examiners with an application for a license to practice nursing is not deductible. In the opinion of the Internal Revenue Service, this is an expenditure to establish qualifications to practice and not an ordinary and necessary expense of practicing. This licensure application fee is nondeductible for the same reason that the expenses of an undergraduate nursing education are nondeductible. However, once the nurse is licensed, periodic license renewal fees are fully deductible, since they are ordinary and necessary expenses of maintaining her professional status. Here the analogy is to the refresher course, expenses of which are deductible because the nurse is maintaining her qualifications and ability to practice.

POLITICAL CONTRIBUTIONS. Although Congress has periodically considered proposals to permit deductions for political contributions, such contributions are not deductible at the present time.

EMPLOYMENT EXPENSES. There are a number of expenses involved in employment or in seeking employment that are deductible for the nurse. Fees paid by the nurse to secure employment are fully deductible. Amounts paid by a nurse to a nurses' registry are conceded to be fully deductible. Contributions by a nurse to a state unemployment insurance fund are also deductible. At the present time this tax applies only in Alabama, Alaska, California, New Jersey, New York, and Rhode Island and in all cases the deduction is allowed from adjusted gross income and not in computing adjusted gross income.

A government employee's transportation and living expenses while away from home in connection with employment are deductible and amounts spent in excess of reimbursement amounts or per diem allowances are also deductible. The same is true of nurses employed by public agencies or by hospitals and physicians.

If the nurse has to pay a doctor or hospital for breakage of equipment, such expenses are fully deductible.

PROFESSIONAL LIABILITY INSURANCE.   Premiums on professional liability insurance are deductible.

UNIFORMS.   The purchase and maintenance of uniforms, including laundry expenses, are deductible expenses for the nurse when the uniform is clearly not the same as ordinary street clothing.

STATIONERY AND OFFICE SUPPLIES.   A private duty nurse can deduct the costs of stationery, office supplies, telephone, stamps, etc., when such expenses were incurred in the course of conducting her practice.

MEALS.   In general a nurse cannot deduct the cost of evening meals she is required to buy near her place of employment because she works late. The Internal Revenue Service (Rev. Rul. 63-239) has announced that it will continue to follow its general rule that costs of meals on one day trips that are not overnight will not be deductible. This is in spite of a recent United States Court of Appeals decision that the trip need not be overnight for the meals to be deductible (Commissioner v. Hanson, 298 F. 2d 391).

CHILD CARE EXPENSES.   Section 214 of the Internal Revenue Code states that the costs of child care to permit a mother to work are deductible to a limited extent. Child care deductions for expenses actually incurred are allowable to the extent of $600 per year for one child and $900 per year for two or more children, provided that the maximum adjusted gross income of the two parents comes to no more than $6,600 and $6,900, respectively. The child care deductions apply only to dependent children under age 13, or to those physically or mentally unable to care for themselves regardless of age. If the nurse is married she cannot take child care deductions unless she files a joint return with her husband.

MOVING EXPENSES.   The Internal Revenue Code provides that moving expenses paid or incurred during the taxable year in connection with the commencement of work by the taxpayer as an employee at a new principal place of work shall be allowed as a deduction. No deductions are allowed unless the new place of work is at least 20 miles further from the former residence than the former place of work. This is a complete change from the old rule which did not permit the deduction of moving and travel expenses when an individual changed his place of employment.

A Checklist of Deductible Expenses

All the ordinary and necessary expenses incurred in the practice of nursing are deductible unless they are otherwise nondeductible as personal expenses. In any given situation the "ordinary and necessary" test can be applied to determine whether a particular expense is personal (non-deductible) or a business (deductible) expense. The emphasis in this checklist are those deductible expenses which are peculiar to the nurse.

Automobile expenses to extent that car is used for professional purposes (not including commuting).

Traveling expenses (not including commuting).

Educational expenses.

Professional meeting costs, including registration fees, room, meals.

Dues and fees to professional societies.

Books, journals, and periodicals, professional.

License reregistration fees.

Employment fees.

Costs of defending professional liability lawsuits.

Premiums on professional liability insurance.

Uniforms, purchase and maintenance.

Child care expenses.

Moving expenses.

21   *Child Abuse Laws*

Some fifty years after enacting the first legislation protecting animals from cruelty, the legislatures of the fifty states began to give consideration to the protection of children from cruelty. In the past few years almost every state has enacted a "battered child" or "child abuse" law. Perhaps the natural reluctance of the courts and state agencies to interfere with the family entity accounts for the fact that until the past few years such agencies were reluctant to take official notice of the fact that children are physically abused, often by their parents.

The child abuse statutes generally fall within the range of permissive legislation and mandatory legislation. In general, permissive legislation protects the doctor or the other member of the healing arts, while mandatory legislation protects the child. Mandatory legislation requires that the practitioner of the healing arts report all cases of child abuse to a named governmental agency. The law is mandatory inasmuch as it states that the practitioner *must* report child abuse or child neglect. If the practitioner does not make the report, he is technically in violation of the law. No case has been found where a doctor or other practitioner of the healing arts was held in violation of law because of failure to report a case of child abuse and it is unlikely that there will be many claims brought against practitioners on these grounds. The mandatory provision in the child abuse law gives the practitioner a firm basis on which to make a report, especially if he is making the report without the knowledge of the parent.

Permissive legislation provides the practitioner with protection against being sued for libel, malpractice, invasion of privacy, etc., or otherwise being held libel to the parent for making the report of child abuse, and usually provides that the practitioner making such a report has no legal liability to the child, parent or guardian, or any other person because of the report. The best child abuse statute is obviously that which combines the mandatory and permissive features, requiring that he make the report and providing him with legal protection for doing so.

The child abuse laws generally apply to all practitioners of the healing professions, although a number of the laws specifically mention the practitioners to whom they apply. The nurse is undeniably included when the law refers to the healing professions, and when the law names specific professions the nurse is specifically included. A nurse should assume that there is a child abuse law in her state or province and govern her conduct accordingly. The nurse working under the direct supervision of a physician probably fulfills her responsibility by notifying the physician of her observations and suggesting that the abuse be reported. The nurse not acting under the direct supervision of the doctor should consider her obligation to make an independent report. It is interesting to note that some of the child abuse statutes have been amended to require that reports of child abuse be reported by all persons and not just those engaged in the healing arts.

The statutes also specify the agency to which the report should be made. In the event of uncertainty the report should be made to the nearest state child welfare agency, and in the absence of such an agency, to the police. There may be some doubt as to what constitutes child abuse although the laws were inspired by situations where it was obvious that the parent had physically injured the child to some extent that was clearly past mere "spanking." The best definitions of child abuse refer to the situations in which children have suffered some physical injury or physical injuries resulting from abuse or neglect occurring from other than accidental means.

22 *Crimes*

The legal relations discussed in previous chapters have been generally limited to the operation of the law as it governs two or more individuals and their respective legal rights and responsibilities to each other. Now our discussion shifts to the individual's legal obligations to the state, which shall be considered to mean any duly constituted political body having the authority to enact ordinances, codes, laws, statutes, or any other legal rules that are binding upon the inhabitants of the area. The basic feature of these rules is that they govern the relation of the individual to the state, and their violation can result in a fine or imprisonment.

We assume that there is no need to instruct the nurse to refrain from committing or participating in a criminal act, but the nurse may not always be aware of the fact that a particular act is criminal. The intent to do evil is not necessarily a prerequisite for the commission of a criminal act, and failure to appreciate the criminal nature of an act may not be a valid defense in a prosecution for commission of a criminal act.

What is a Crime?

In its simplest form a crime is a positive or negative act in violation of penal law; an offense against the state. Some of the other legal definitions of a crime are:

Any act done in violation of those duties which an individual owes to the community, and for which the law has provided that the offender shall make satisfaction to the public.

A crime or public offense is an act committed or omitted in violation of a law forbidding it or commanding it, and to which is annexed, upon conviction, either of the following punishments: (1) death, (2) imprisonment, (3) fine, (4) removal from office, or (5) disqualification to hold and enjoy any office or honor, trust or profit in the state.

A crime is a violation of the public right and of duties due to the whole community considered as such, and in its social and aggregate capacity.

A crime, as opposed to a civil injury, is the violation of a right, considered in reference to the evil tendency of such violation, as regards the community at large.

One of the rudiments of English, American, and Canadian law is that there are no such things as *ex post facto* crimes in their systems of government. An act that was lawful when committed cannot be rendered unlawful by some subsequent act of a judicial or legislative body. The government, at all levels, does not possess the authority to enact and enforce criminal laws having retroactive effect.

Intent

A crime may be committed even though the wrongdoer did not intend that a particular event would take place or that a criminal law would be violated. For example, the crime of homicide, the unlawful killing of another, does not require for a conviction that the wrongdoer intended that someone would die. In many instances the difference between murder and manslaughter is the difference between the presence or absence of criminal intent. This does not always hold true, however, as many laws provide that if any death results during the commission of a felony the wrongdoer will be held to have committed a murder even though there was no intent to cause a death.

The legal definitions of motive and criminal intent are quite complex. A criminal motive is defined as the inducement existing in the minds of persons causing them to intend and afterward to commit a crime. Criminal intent is defined as the intent to commit a crime. It could be said that the crimes against a person do not require proof of a criminal intent but that crimes against property do require proof of criminal intent. Larceny is a good example of a crime which requires that criminal intent be proved as an essential element of a prosecution. Larceny may be defined as the felonious taking of personal property without the consent of the other and with intent to convert to the use of the taker. If the taker does not have this intent—if he picks up someone else's property without any intent to do so—he has not committed the crime of larceny. However if one finds the property of another and converts it to his own use, he has committed larceny at the time that he knows or should have known the identity of the true owner and intends to deprive the owner of his property.

It may seem to the nurse that this discussion is out of place, that we should be able to expect that the professional nurse would not commit criminal acts. The problem is that the nurse may find herself participating in a criminal act without any premeditation or criminal intent. Consider the situation in which a patient leaves some property behind in the doctor's office or a hospital room. The property could be money, jewelry or anything else of value. The nurse is not free to "find" this property and keep it. If she makes a logical attempt to find the owner and cannot, then she has no criminal intent; if she keeps the property when she knows the owner, or when she should be able to ascertain the owner, she has criminal intent and is guilty of larceny.

In most instances the presence or absence of intent is proved by circumstantial evidence. The question of intent is really the question of what is in an individual's mind at the time he commits an act. This is extremely difficult to prove—the wrongdoer may not be willing to state what was in his mind at a particular time or he may not be able to do so. Intent must be proved by the acts of the individual, rather than by an attempt to engage in some psychoanalytical process. If the nurse finds money in a hospital room soon after the patient has checked out of the room and the nurse does not make any effort to contact the patient, her failure to act would itself be evidence of criminal intent.

Classes of Crimes

The violation of a federal statute, a state statute, or a municipal or county ordinance constitutes a crime. In addition there are so-called common law crimes. In many states the courts have said that there are no such things as common law crimes, i.e., the only crimes are those specifically stated in a statute or ordinance. In some jurisdictions the common law crime is recognized only to the extent of misdemeanors. The difficulty with common law crimes is that they are not legislative enactments; they are judge-made criminal rules, or sometimes mere traditional rules of criminal conduct. They are often ill-defined and so vague that they present a danger of misinterpretation. In general it is desirable that the whole concept of common law crimes be eliminated from our system of law. In this chapter there shall be little or no significance attached to so-called common law crimes. According to Blackstone the word "crime" denotes such offenses as are of a deeper and more serious nature, while smaller transgressions of limited consequence are known as misdemeanors. However a more modern approach is to use the term "crime" to encompass both felonies and misdemeanors. Thus under common usage the violation of a motor vehicle ordinance restricting speed would constitute a crime. One would have to look at the nature of the crime to determine whether or not it is a felony or a misdemeanor.

A simple distinction between a felony and a misdemeanor is that the felony is an act punishable by death or imprisonment in a penitentiary— everything else is a misdemeanor. The felony is obviously the more serious classification of crimes. The typical misdemeanor would be traffic law violations and other such small crimes that would result in a short jail sentence or a fine. The term felony has no definite or precise meaning other than that provided, except when it is specifically defined in the statute which provides that a certain act is a felony. As a general rule a crime is not a felony unless it is so designated by the statute that defines the crime or by a statement that the crime is punishable by death or imprisonment. The term felony is an inheritance from English law where it originally meant that the individual had forfeited his property and real estate to the king upon conviction of certain offenses. From this came the term forfeiture and then felony. In number, there are more misdemeanor statutes than felony statutes, although felonies are definitely more important. Nursing and medical practice acts often provide that an individual practicing medicine or nursing without a license shall be fined a sum and sentenced to not more than 30 days in jail. This means that the practice acts are misdeameanor statutes and the person who has violated the practice act by engaging in practice without a license has committed a misdemeanor. In some states the practice acts provide for sentencing to a penitentiary making them felony statutes. In some cases the first offense is treated as a misdemeanor but repeated offenses of unlicensed practice are treated as felonies.

There are two schools of thought on whether the nursing practice acts should provide that unlicensed practice should constitute a felony or a misdemeanor. Most persons agree that the seriousness of unlicensed practice of nursing or medicine requires the more severe penalties imposed by a felony statute, which is difficult to disagree with. However, the fact that the statute provides for a felony may deter a jury from voting for a conviction. The jury may be willing to subject the accused to a short jail sentence or a fine for this transgression but may feel that they would rather acquit the accused than find him guilty of a felony requiring a prison sentence. The distinction between a felony and a misdemeanor is important to the nurse in other contexts. Most jurisdictions have statutes which provide that if death results from the commission of a felony the wrongdoer will be guilty of murder even if he had no intention that a death result. Consider the situation in which the nurse participates in an illegal abortion and the patient dies as a result. For the sake of making this point we will assume that the nurse acted with good intent and the death was a result of no fault on the part of the physician or nurse. If the state law makes the performance of this abortion a felony, the nurse and doctor are guilty of murder even though they provided a high level of care and the death was not a result of their malfeasance.

Conspiracy

In addition to the commission of a criminal act, conspiring to commit an unlawful act is a separate and distinct crime. A conspiracy has been defined as a combination or confederacy of two or more persons formed for the purpose of committing, by their joint efforts, some unlawful or criminal act, or some act which is innocent in itself, but becomes unlawful when done by the concerted action of the conspirators; or for the purpose of using criminal or unlawful means to the commission of an act not itself unlawful.

To prove the crime of conspiracy it is unnecessary to prove that there was some overt act toward accomplishment of the unlawful purpose. The existence of a conspiracy may be proved not only by direct evidence but also by inference from concurrent statements, facts, or circumstances that disclose a common design on the part of the accused and others to act in pursuance of a common criminal purpose. A conspiracy is completed when an agreement is made and there has been a common criminal intent. The purpose need not be accomplished for the participating parties to be guilty of a conspiracy. In a conspiracy each of the parties is liable for the acts of the other.

Crimes in the Medical Office

As a member of the community, the nurse has a legal duty to avoid violation of penal laws so that she is not guilty of a crime. She also has the protection of the penal laws so that she will not be a victim of another violating the penal laws. If the nurse violates the penal law and is convicted of a crime she risks death, fine, or imprisonment. If the nurse is a victim of a crime she does not receive any personal recompensation since the law provides only that the guilty party suffer death, fine, or imprisonment. If the nurse wishes financial recompense against the individual who has committed the crime her sole recourse is a civil lawsuit against the guilty party. It is interesting to note that some countries, United States and Canada not included, are experimenting with a system whereby the state will make financial restitution to the victim of a criminal act. This is a very modern approach as it takes cognizance of the fact that the victim often cannot get any financial recompense against the guilty party because that person has no financial means. Insurance does not usually come into play here because any insurance coverage that the guilty party maintains would usually contain an exclusion for a criminal or other voluntary act.

The nurse as a private citizen is subject to the same criminal codes as other persons. However there are a number of situations having legal implications to which the nurse may be exposed that are not presented to laymen. There are two distinctive factors of criminal law as it exists in the medical office or the hospital. In most situations criminal law is the clearest of all laws, and rightfully so, but when we get to the areas of criminal abortion or other crimes in the medical office we find an unusual vagueness. This is undoubtedly due to the fact that there have been a minimum of prosecutions for medical office crimes. This may be a result of the fact that such crimes are ignored by the courts on the basis that the criminal laws on the subject are unreasonable. Many of the medical office crimes are not crimes in the minds of most persons. This is especially true in some areas of dispensing narcotics and performing so-called illegal abortions. In some of these areas good medical practice appears to be more modern than the law and it is no wonder that sometimes the criminal law is not enforced when it is contrary to good medical practice.

Violation of Drug Laws

Perhaps the greatest problem area for the nurse is with respect to the criminal aspects of the federal and the state narcotics laws. These are generally criminal laws providing severe penalties for violation. It should also be noted that perhaps the most common grounds for revocation of a professional nurse's license stated in the state nursing practice acts is the unlawful dispensing of narcotics.

The Harrison Narcotics Act, a part of the Internal Revenue Code, provides that it shall be unlawful for an individual to dispense narcotics unless that person has been registered under the act. Annual reregistration is also required. The cost of registration and reregistration is only one dollar per year so it is obvious that the purpose of requiring registration is to regulate the dispensing of narcotics rather than the collection of an insignificant amount of tax revenue. The law specifically states that physicians, dentists, veterinary surgeons, and other practitioners who are lawfully entitled to distribute, dispense, or administer narcotics must comply with the registration requirement. The narcotics law also provides some indication that the physician or dentist has no authority to delegate the administration of a narcotic. It provides in part for an exemption for the doctor from the operation of some parts of the narcotics law when he dispenses or distributes narcotics to a patient "upon whom such doctor shall personally attend."

It is clear from a reading of the federal narcotics law that the nurse may not distribute or dispense narcotic drugs. If she does, she has performed a criminal act by dispensing narcotics without being registered under the law, and it is no defense that the nurse is not eligible for registration under the narcotics law. The sale of narcotics to addicts, the provision of prescriptions to addicts, or the preparation and distribution of prescriptions that are fictitious or fraudulent in any manner are also criminal acts. The nurse foolish enough to provide an addict with narcotics or a falsified prescription has committed an illegal act. As a general rule it is best for the nurse to exclude narcotics completely from her areas of interest or practice and keep herself as distant from this phase of medical practice as possible.

If narcotics are stolen from the doctor's office the nurse may wish to remind the doctor of his legal obligation to immediately notify the nearest office of the Internal Revenue Service. The doctor will have to submit a sworn statement of the facts of the theft, a list of the narcotics stolen, and a statement that he called the police as soon as he found that the narcotics had been stolen.

In addition to the Harrison Narcotics Act there are state narcotics laws in all states, most of which are state enactments of the Uniform State Narcotics Law. None of the state laws broadens the nurse's authority or lack of authority to dispense narcotics, and the effect of the state law is to impose additional requirements in record keeping and in the use of proper forms for purchasing and dispensing narcotics.

Abortions

Another offense for which a nursing license can be revoked is "willfully violating or knowingly assisting in the violation of any law of the state relating to the practice of abortion."

Under no circumstances is a nurse legally entitled to perform an abortion, and if the nurse is foolish enough to do so she has undoubtedly committed a criminal act. If the patient dies during the abortion it is very likely that the nurse will be considered to be guilty of murder.

One problem in discussing abortion laws is the fact that there is a wide divergence between the states in the definition of "illegal abortion." The problem is in the definition of an "illegal abortion" rather than the definition of an "abortion," because the latter term is easily defined in the law, and from a legal standpoint there is no difference between a miscarriage and an abortion. Although there is a medical difference between these terms, under the abortion statutes they are usually treated as the same.

Illegal abortions are defined in most state laws by stating that all abortions are illegal abortions except those caused for specified reasons.

The most common exemption (thus making the abortion legal) is for the preservation of the life of the patient. Some states are more liberal and provide that an abortion is not illegal if the conception arose out of an illegal act, if the patient was the victim of rape or incest, or if a live birth would have a severe effect on the mental health of the patient. The State of Colorado, in early 1967, was one of the first states to liberalize its abortion law and it is expected that many other states will follow this example. The Board of Trustees of the American Medical Association has recently recommended a general liberalization of these laws.

From the physician's point of view there is a major problem caused by the fact that a technical reading of the state law would make a particular abortion illegal while good medical practice would seem to indicate the desirability of an abortion. It is a well accepted fact that the majority of the abortions performed in the United States are probably illegal but are a result of good medical practice insofar as the mental health of the patient is concerned. A complicating factor when a doctor decides to perform an illegal abortion for the well-being of his patient is that most state laws provide that "if the death of the woman results from the abortion the person procuring or causing the abortion is guilty of murder." The moral questions must be put aside in this discussion for obvious reasons.

The whole area of abortions as criminal acts is confusing and especially so for the nurse, because the laws dealing with abortions are usually unrealistic, and because the nurse participating in an abortion usually does so as an assistant to a physician. There are at least four different criminal laws involved in the commission of an abortion and the nurse is involved in these crimes even when she is not the one actually causing the abortion. The four "crimes" are:

(1) commission of an illegal abortion;
(2) attempting to commit an illegal abortion;
(3) conspiracy in the commission of an illegal abortion;
(4) being an accomplice in the commission of an illegal abortion.

The nurse who commits an illegal abortion by herself is obviously guilty of a crime. The other three crimes could be committed when the nurse is performing her customary nursing duties in assisting a physician, or when she actively participates in the abortion.

The commission of a crime is a separate crime from an attempt to commit a crime. Stated another way, it is a separate crime to attempt to commit a crime. Under most statutes, causing an abortion and attempting to produce an abortion are separate and distinct criminal offenses. This means that if the nurse, doctor or other person fails to perform the abortion after making an attempt, he has committed a crime even though the abortion did not occur.

A conspiracy to commit a criminal act is also a separate and distinct crime. If the nurse assists or participates in a conspiracy by arranging for the abortion, she has committed the crime of participating in a conspiracy to commit an illegal act. The nurse may be found to be participating in the conspiracy merely by making an appointment when she knows the purpose of the meeting, or in recommending to a patient that a particular doctor will perform an illegal abortion.

The most difficult problem arises when the nurse is subject to the criminal charge that she was an accomplice in the commission of an illegal abortion. An accomplice is one who unites in the commission of a crime. The nurse who participates in an illegal abortion by assisting the physician performing the abortion is herself performing an illegal or criminal act. This may create an impossible situation for the nurse when she is directed by the physician to participate and she does not know whether or not she is being asked to participate in an illegal abortion. The problem can become even more complicated when the nurse knows that the act is criminal but believes that it is not immoral or undesirable. It should be recalled that the provision for revocation of a nurse's professional license includes, in some states, "knowingly assisting in the violation of any law of the state relating to the practice of abortion."

Criminal Malpractice

Although the subject of malpractice is generally a civil matter between the nurse and the injured person, a nurse may be prosecuted for criminal malpractice. This is not a very common basis for criminal actions against health practitioners although it is provided for in the laws of many states.

A prosecution for criminal malpractice might be brought when the patient has died as a result of the malpractice. The prosecution would probably be brought on the basis of involuntary homicide or manslaughter, which is a felony in most states. The penalty is usually substantially less severe than it is for voluntary homicide or murder. The element of malpractice causing the death of the patient would have to be so great that the law would consider it to be grounds for a criminal prosecution. As stated before, this is a rare proceeding and is usually limited to the situation in which the patient has died from a malpractice action so gross as to be an indication of total disregard for the life or safety of another.

Experimentation

No more than a brief discussion is needed for the nurse to appreciate the fact that human experimentation must not be performed in the hospital or medical office without the full knowledge and consent of the patient. If an experiment is performed and the patient is physically injured the patient would have a cause of action in a civil suit for damages based upon assault. In addition there would be grounds for a criminal suit for battery, the physical harm to another caused without that person's permission and not otherwise justified or excused under the criminal law. If the patient voluntarily participated in the experiment after knowing all the facts and the dangers present he would not be able to bring a successful civil suit and there undoubtedly would not be a criminal action. If the patient did not give his consent or was not informed of the nature of the experiment, or if the patient was not old enough to have the capacity to consent, then the resulting injury could give rise to a criminal prosecution for battery.

The doctor and nurse may not always realize that they are conducting an experiment. Any time a procedure or medication used has not been sufficiently tested so as to be in accepted usage, an experiment is being performed. This is true even though the doctor and nurse act in the best professional manner in performing the experiment with the patient's best interests as their sole objective.

Unauthorized Autopsy

In addition to the rights of the relatives to bring civil suit for an unauthorized autopsy, the laws of many states make it a criminal act for anyone to perform an unauthorized autopsy. Although few nurses are involved in this procedure the nurse assisting a physician or another person in performing an unauthorized autopsy may be committing a criminal act, conspiring to commit a criminal act, or may be an accomplice to the commission of a criminal act.

Liability for Criminal Acts of Another

Generally, one individual is not liable for the criminal acts of another unless he directed or participated in the criminal act. The nurse is not liable for the criminal acts of the physician, for example, in performing an abortion or providing narcotics to an addict, but she may be guilty of the separate criminal act of conspiring to commit a crime or being an accomplice in the commission of a crime.

The physician is not criminally responsible for the criminal acts of the nurse even though the acts were committed on behalf of the doctor. For example, if the nurse commits a theft of medical supplies for the doctor without his knowledge and consent, the doctor is not liable for her actions. The doctor would be liable for the nurse's criminal actions only if he directs that the nurse act in a criminal manner or if the crime is committed in a situation under his control when he knew or should have known that a crime was being committed.

Births and Deaths

Under the laws of most states it is a criminal act, usually a misdemeanor, for the person in attendance at a birth or death to fail to report the event to the proper authorities. If a physician is present in either situation the duty is obviously his. If no physician is present, the nurse, especially if she is serving as a midwife, must make the report. Local laws vary substantially in this regard so the nurse should become familiar with the law in her locale.

Contraceptive Information and Devices

A few states, notably Connecticut and Massachusetts, have antiquated statutes making the provision of contraceptive information and devices a crime. Nurses working in these two states should take special care to familiarize themselves with the state law on this subject.

Summary

The practice of professional and practical nursing has not presented any significant amount of problems of criminal law. The areas discussed in this chapter have been presented for their general interest and to warn the nurse of the general application of criminal law and the particular criminal law questions presented in nursing practice. Statistically speaking, the nursing profession has been beyond reproach in being able to keep itself in step with criminal law.

Appendix A

EXAMINATION FOR STATE LICENSURE TO PRACTICE NURSING*

WHY IS LICENSURE NECESSARY?

The protection of the public is the basic purpose of all licensing legislation. All states control the practice of nursing by law.

Individuals desiring to practice nursing must meet the qualifications and standards established through state law. Provision is made to revoke or suspend the license of anyone who fails to function in accordance with the standards prescribed.

Each profession has a social responsibility to protect the public through establishing and maintaining its individual standards for education and for practice. The public cannot be expected to differentiate between competent and incompetent practitioners.

The American Nurses' Association is the organization representing licensed professional nurses. After its establishment in 1896, state nurses associations were formed, and they promoted the enactment of laws controlling the practice of nursing. The American Nurses' Association believes that mandatory laws are essential for public safety.†

WHAT DOES THE NURSE GAIN FROM LICENSURE?

1. She may legally practice nursing in the state in which she is currently licensed.

2. She may apply for licensure by endorsement in a second state or in a foreign country.

3. The professional nurse is eligible for membership in the state nurses association, the American Nurses' Association and the International Council of Nurses.

4. The practical nurse is eligible for membership in the National Federation of Licensed Practical Nurses.

---

* Publication of the American Nurses' Association.
† See ANA Legislation Manual for Committees on Legislation of State Nurses Association.

WHAT IS THE LICENSING AUTHORITY IN EACH STATE?

The laws of each state provide for the appointment of a board of nursing, which is a unit of state government. The ANA recommends that the board be composed of professional nurses meeting specified qualifications.[*]

HOW DOES THE BOARD OF NURSING FUNCTION?

Basic responsibilities of boards of nursing are:

1. Establishment of minimum standards for programs in basic nursing—both professional and practical.

2. Visitation of schools and study of curriculum, faculty and facilities as a prerequisite to the granting of official accreditation.

3. Development of licensing examinations to test the fitness of candidates in meeting minimum standards of safety to practice.

4. Administration of the examination and, on the basis of candidate achievement, determination of the granting or withholding of a license.

5. Arrangement for the periodic renewal of licenses.

6. Suspension or revocation of licenses for cause.

7. Maintenance of legal records.

8. Action on applications for licensure from candidates from other states and other countries.

9. Collection, analysis and interpretation of data on education and licensure.

10. Stimulation for improvement in nursing and nursing education.

HOW IS THE EXAMINATION PREPARED
AND ADMINISTERED?

Candidates for licensure apply to the board of nursing in the particular state in which they wish to practice. If the application is approved by the board of nursing, the applicant is eligible to take the state licensing examination. Since the purpose of the examination is to determine minimum competency for safe practice, the same examination is used for all graduates, although preparation may vary in diploma, associate degree and baccalaureate programs.

In response to the need for more rapid scoring of examination papers,

---

[*] See ANA Manual for Members of State Boards of Nursing.

the boards of nursing, working through the American Nurses' Association and the Committee on Tests in Nursing of the National League for Nursing Education, created in 1944 the first State Board Test Pool Examination which could be machine scored. The National League for Nursing Education made an outstanding contribution to this project.

The plan has been continued by the ANA Committee of State Boards of Nursing with the help and services of the NLN Test Construction Unit and the Evaluation Service.

The ANA Committee of State Boards of Nursing appoints a Committee on Blueprint for Licensing Examinations, composed of six persons employed by state boards from different geographical regions of the United States. This committee develops a core test plan for each series of professional and practical nursing examinations. Subject matter experts (item writers) are recommended by all state boards on an alternating basis to prepare suitable items for the tests. Each item writer spends one week working with the NLN Test Construction staff to formulate questions in the area of her specialty. The professional nursing examination includes five subjects—medical, surgical, obstetric, pediatric and psychiatric nursing.

Each paper includes 100 to 120 multiple choice questions designed not only to test specific knowledge but also the ability to apply that knowledge in making judgments concerning the care of the patient.

The Blueprint Committee reviews and compiles the work of the item writers, and a draft of the proposed questions is sent to each board of nursing. Under strict security regulations, the board members study the questions and indicate the items they believe should be retained, revised or deleted. Constructive criticism of the entire document is given.

Following a final review by the Blueprint Committee, the examination papers are printed in final form by the National League for Nursing. They are then distributed to the participating boards of nursing under signed contracts which provide for security regulations and the financial agreement.

The examination in practical nursing is developed in two parts, according to a similar plan. Knowledge and judgment necessary to pass this examination are in keeping with the minimum standards for practical nursing.

Two days are allowed for writing the examination in professional nursing and one day for the examination in practical nursing.

The candidates' answer sheets are returned to the NLN for machine-scoring, and statistical reports are sent to each board of nursing. The board studies the results and determines the minimum passing score.

Responsibility for determining the passing score and deciding whether or not the candidate may be safely granted licensure is thus carried by the individual board of nursing. Candidates who qualify are granted a license to practice. Others are advised about repeating the tests in which they have failed.

The following is a sample of the type of question which might be used on an examination in professional nursing.

If a patient with diabetes mellitus becomes anxious and perspires and complains of weakness and hunger, which action is it important for the nurse to take?
1. Put him to bed and apply extra warmth.
2. Obtain a urine specimen.
3. Take his blood pressure, pulse and respiration.
4. Give him a beverage containing sugar.

HOW IS A LICENSE OBTAINED IN A SECOND STATE?

A nurse licensed in one state who wishes to practice in a second state makes application to the board of nursing in the second state. The latter board will review the information submitted and determine if a license may be granted by endorsement without examination, if examination is indicated, or if supplementary courses must be taken. The board must be assured that the preparation of the applicant is the equivalent of that required in the state.

HOW IS A LICENSE OBTAINED BY A NURSE FROM ANOTHER COUNTRY?

A nurse licensed in another country makes application to the board of nursing in the state in which she wishes to work. She must supply proof of completion of a program in nursing accredited by the official agency in her country. The board evaluates the credentials and determines whether its minimum requirements are met. Citizenship or declaration of intention is a prerequisite for licensure in several states.*

GENERAL INFORMATION

1. All candidates for licensure in professional nursing in all states

---

* See Facts About Nursing, 1960. Table 8, page 53.

must have completed the twelfth grade or the equivalent; requirements in practical nursing differ in the various states.

2. State board examinations are given in all states at least once a year. Each board sets its own deadline for acceptance of applications.

3. Dates of examinations are published in the American Journal of Nursing and in local publications.

4. Examination centers are determined by the board.

5. Fees for the licensing examination range from \$10 to \$30.*

6. Fees are payable in advance.

7. Some state laws have requirements regarding citizenship and minimum age.†

STATE BOARDS OF NURSING

ALABAMA	State Administration Bldg., Montgomery 4
ALASKA	Box 4-776, Spenard
ARIZONA	427 State Capital Bldg., Phoenix
ARKANSAS	314 W. Markham St., Little Rock
CALIFORNIA	1021 O St., Sacramento 14
COLORADO	Rm. 127, 1525 Sherman St., Denver 3
CONNECTICUT	State Office Bldg., Rm. 357, Hartford
DELAWARE	2 E. 14th St., Wilmington
DISTRICT OF COLUMBIA	1740 Mass. Ave., N.W., Washington 6
FLORIDA	Rm. 6, 230 W. Forsyth St., Jacksonville 2
GEORGIA	116 Mitchell St., S.W., Atlanta 3
HAWAII	Iolani Barracks, Honolulu 13
IDAHO	216 N. 8th St., Box 2067, Boise
ILLINOIS	160 N. LaSalle St., Chicago 1
INDIANA	100 N. Senate Ave., Indianapolis 4
IOWA	State Office Bldg., Rm. 628, Des Moines
KANSAS	State Office Bldg., Topeka
KENTUCKY	600 West Cedar St., Louisville 2
LOUISIANA	407 State Office Bldg., New Orleans
MAINE	363 Main St., Lewiston
MARYLAND	301 W. Preston St., Baltimore 1
MASSACHUSETTS	38 State House, Boston 33
MICHIGAN	148 Stevens T. Mason Bldg., Lansing 26
MINNESOTA	700 Minnesota Bldg., St. Paul 1

---

* See Facts About Nursing, 1960, page 52.
† See Facts About Nursing, 1960, page 53.

MISSISSIPPI	703 North St., Jackson 2
MISSOURI	235 State Capitol Bldg., Jefferson City
MONTANA	1411 Helena Ave., Helena
NEBRASKA	State Capitol Bldg., Lincoln 9
NEVADA	P. O. Box 1884, Reno
NEW HAMPSHIRE	4 Park St., Concord
NEW JERSEY	1100 Raymond Blvd., Newark 2
NEW MEXICO	107 Stanford Drive, S.E., Albuquerque
NEW YORK	The State Education Dept., Albany 1
NORTH CAROLINA	Box 2129 Raleigh
NORTH DAKOTA	State Capitol, Bismarck
OHIO	240 S. Parsons Avenue, Columbus 15
OKLAHOMA	1101 Cravens Bldg., Oklahoma City 2
OREGON	1400 S.W. 5th Ave., Portland 1
PENNSYLVANIA	Education Bldg., Harrisburg
PUERTO RICO	452 Comercio St., San Juan
RHODE ISLAND	366 State Office Bldg., Providence 2
SOUTH CAROLINA	809 Carolina Life Bldg., Columbia 1
SOUTH DAKOTA	Box 836, Mitchell
TENNESSEE	1110 Sudekum Bldg., Nashville 3
TEXAS	614 W. Sixth St., Austin 1
UTAH	316-A State Capitol, Salt Lake City 14
VERMONT	323 Pearl Street, Burlington
VIRGINIA	1110 Central Nat'l. Bank Bldg., Richmond 19
VIRGIN ISLANDS	Charlotte Amalie, St. Thomas
WASHINGTON	Dept. of Licenses, Olympia
WEST VIRGINIA	910 Quarrier St., Charleston 1
WISCONSIN	119 Monona Ave., Rm. 607, Madison 3
WYOMING	Box 856, Laramie

Appendix B

INTERPRETATION OF THE STATEMENTS OF THE CODE FOR PROFESSIONAL NURSES*

INTRODUCTION

The development of a code of ethics is an essential characteristic of a profession, and provides one means whereby professional standards may be established, maintained, and improved. A code indicates a profession's acceptance of the responsibility and trust with which it has been invested. Each practitioner, upon entering a profession, inherits a measure of that responsibility and trust and the obligation they impose for ethical practice and conduct.

> The public expects ethical practice and conduct from professional men, and it is angered by violations of standards which it assumes ordinarily control practice. Each violation diminishes trust. Without trust, a profession would perish.†

The Code for Professional Nurses was adopted by the American Nurses' Association in 1950, and revised in 1960. It is intended as a guide for the professional practice, conduct, and relationships of the nurse. The preamble "Professional status in nursing is maintained and enriched by the willingness of the individual practitioner to accept and fulfill obligations to society, co-workers, and the profession of nursing" indicates the three areas of ethical concern into which the statements of the *Code* are loosely grouped.

The first statement of the *Code*, "The fundamental responsibility of the nurse is to conserve life, to alleviate suffering, and to promote health" brings the nurse's responsibility to the public and the individual patient immediately into focus as the basis for determining all professional conduct and relationships. It is hoped that this is clearly reflected throughout the interpretation of the *Code* on the following pages.

Upholding the *Code* personally and seeing that colleagues do so is part of the moral obligation of every professional nurse. Guidance and

---

* Publication of the American Nurses' Association.

† McGlothin, William J. *Patterns of Professional Education.* New York: G. P. Putnam's Sons, 1960, p. 211.

191

assistance in implementing the *Code* in local situations may be obtained from state committees on nursing practice.

Further information about the interpretation of the *Code* may be obtained from the ANA Committee on Ethical Standards.

1. The fundamental responsibility of the nurse is to conserve life, to alleviate suffering, and to promote health.

Service to mankind, in relation to health and well-being, is the primary function of nursing. Nurses are employed to use their knowledge and skills, either directly or indirectly, to conserve life, alleviate suffering, or promote health, and this basic responsibility to patients determines their professional relationships. If otherwise employed, they should avoid the use of titles and symbols associated with nursing.

Concern for health and well-being of the patient establishes the ethical responsibility of the nurse to take all possible steps to insure that the highest standards of nursing care are maintained. Conditions in the work situation that prevent the nurse from using skills and knowledge to the best advantage for the patient should be called to the attention of those who are in position to help eradicate such conditions. These may be persons in positions of authority within the institution or agency, the state nurses association, or the state board of nursing.

It may be necessary at times for the nurse to balance concern for the patient with responsibilities and relationships as an individual and a citizen. For example, a private duty nurse may be faced with a decision about undertaking a case. A number of circumstances might rightfully affect the nurse's decision. Family obligations, other personal or professional commitments, or perhaps a lack of preparation in some specialized skills needed in the case may be influencing factors. The nurse is ethically justified in giving consideration to such factors and making an individual decision for or against taking employment.

Responsibility for patient care requires that the nurse be prepared to meet emergency situations with understanding and acceptance of the lifesaving nature of the profession. When continuous nursing care is required, the nurse should remain with the patient until assured adequate relief is available. The nurse should also be willing, in an emergency, to perform services essential to patient care usually carried out by nonprofessional personnel, if such action will not contribute to the prolongation of the emergency situation. In the everyday situation, however, the nurse guards that her special abilities are devoted to nursing care and not to functions and activities more properly the concern of others.

In the professional role, and often in private life, the nurse should be aware that acts, bearing, attitudes, and appearance are often viewed by others as examples of health practices. This provides many opportunities for demonstrating how good health is promoted. Even the wearing of the uniform, so closely associated in the public mind with nursing, indicates the nurse's understanding of its role in the protection of the patient. Worn outside the patient unit, the purpose of the uniform is negated if it serves as a carrier of harmful organisms into the patient's environment, from one patient to another, or from the patient's environment to the public.

Each nurse, assuming a part in carrying out the fundamental responsibility of the members of the profession, helps to determine the contribution and impact of the profession on the total health care of the world community.

2. The nurse provides services based on human need, with respect for dignity, unrestricted by considerations of nationality, race, creed, color, or status.

The need for nursing service is universal. Every person, whatever his country, his ethnic identification, his beliefs or living conditions, needs nursing care at some time during his life. Professional nursing service, therefore, should and must be based solely on human need, with respect for the dignity of the individual human being.

The universality of nursing service stands forth in the second statement of the pledge for new graduates based on the International Code of Nursing Ethics, "I promise to care for the sick with all the skill I possess; no matter what their race, creed, color, politics or social status, sparing no effort to conserve life, alleviate pain, and promote health."

Consideration of both the human and medical factors influencing illness are indispensable to planning and carrying out effective nursing care. Productive nurse-patient relationships require recognition of the psychosocial factors that may encourage or inhibit progress toward health.

The nurse uses knowledge of psychology and sociology to assume the initiative in fostering conditions which promote the optimum progress of those entrusted to her care. She seeks an understanding of self and reactions to others and assists patients to positive attitudes about their conditions and treatments. She gives leadership to the establishment of the harmonious relationships with other nurses and members of the health team so necessary to each patient's sense of security, and which reinforce his confidence in those assisting him.

An understanding and acceptance of the customs, attitudes, and beliefs of others enable the nurse to give needed support to patients and contribute to her own growth and maturity. Concerned only with considerations of need, the nurse applies the highest standards of professional care to all who require her services.

3. The nurse does not use professional knowledge and skill in any enterprise detrimental to the public good.

The nurse is continually concerned with upgrading the health care of the public, and does not lend professional status to, or use professional knowledge and skill in any activities which would tend to lower the standards of that care. For example, the nurse does not assist in the promotion of, or teach in, correspondence schools for practical nursing or any other schools that do not meet the standards of the profession or those of the legal bodies responsible for accreditation. Such schools often encourage their students to attempt to carry out nursing functions and activities for which they are not adequately prepared, and thus endanger the public health. Nurses who assist in recruitment or teaching for these schools may be involved in fraudulent enterprises since the quality and results of the programs are often misrepresented to prospective students.

Bearing in mind that along with professional status goes an obligation to protect the public and advance standards, each nurse attempts to insure that the unique contributions of the members of the profession are directed toward safe, high-quality nursing care.

4. The nurse respects and holds in confidence all information of a confidential nature obtained in the course of nursing work unless required by law to divulge it.

The nurse, as well as the physician, has a clear obligation to keep secret any information relating to a patient's illness which she obtains during the performance of her professional duties, unless the patient authorizes her to disclose this information or a competent court orders her to reveal it. This obligation is based first, on the ethics of her profession and second, on the law.*

The plan of nursing care for the patient is the responsibility and privilege of the professional nurse, and knowledge received in confidence may be invaluable in enabling the nurse to plan more effectively or to alter nursing plans, as necessary, to meet specific needs.

Patients often confide in their nurses, sharing anxieties, hopes, fears, and plans about their illnesses and their private and public lives. The nurse receives all information in a nonjudgmental manner, using it to promote the patient's welfare, never to his disadvantage. Recognizing that patients have the right of privacy, the nurse makes known details about the treatment or physical, personal or social condition of a patient only to others who are professionally concerned in a direct way with the patient's health care.

Occasionally, circumstances may arise which place the nurse under obligation to give testimony of a specific nature about a patient. When

---

* Hayt, Emanuel, Lillian R. Hayt, August H. Groeschel, and Dorothy McMillan. *Law of Hospital and Nurse.* New York: Hospital Textbook Co., 1958, p. 304.

a court orders testimony to be given on knowledge of facts in a litigation, the nurse should first obtain information about legal rights and privileges as a professional person in such matters under the laws of the state. Testimony of a confidential nature should never be volunteered, but should be given, when necessary, without elaboration, and kept to the minimum degree necessary to answer the questions of the court.

Cognizant that pain, embarrassment, loss of reputation or position, or other hardships or suffering may result from breach of a patient's confidence, the nurse at all times respects the confidential nature of information received in giving nursing care. Professional judgment is carefully exercised in determining whether information could be of value in promoting the health care of the patient and the person or persons who could best use it in this way.

5. The nurse as a citizen understands and upholds the laws and performs the duties of citizenship; as a professional person the nurse has particular responsibility to work with other citizens and health professions in promoting efforts to meet health needs of the public.

The nurse is a citizen as well as a member of a profession. As a citizen the nurse abides by the laws, performs the duties and enjoys the privileges of citizenship. The nurse must be willing and prepared to protect and use these privileges to insure that they are not lost through ignorance or neglect. As a citizen, the nurse is concerned with all legislation, and contributes interest, support, and leadership toward general improvement of the community.

As a professional person, the nurse's special background enables her to have a greater understanding of the nature of health problems. This understanding imposes a particular responsibility to interpret and speak out in regard to legislation affecting health. The resources of the professional association enables the nurse to work with colleagues in assessing current or pending health legislation and its effect upon the community and to determine the stand that should be taken in the interest of the greatest public good. Sometimes this stand may lead to concerted action with other health groups. At other times, nurses may find it necessary to work alone to support the principles which the profession believes will result in the greatest benefits to patient care.

Through the dual role of citizen and professional person, the nurse promotes those social, economic, and political factors that develop a desirable pattern for living and health in her own locality and the larger community.

6. The nurse has responsibility for membership and participation in the nurses' professional organization.

It has been stated that the professional organization is an organization of practitioners who judge one another as professionally competent and who have banded together to perform social functions which they cannot perform in their separate capacity as individuals.* Membership in the professional organization and responsible participation in its activities are recognized obligations of the practitioners of every profession.

The American Nurses' Association is the professional organization for registered nurses and the one through which they can "speak with one voice" in regard to nursing care and work together to promote those principles and concepts in which they believe, based on their expert knowledge in the field.

Each nurse assumes responsibility for membership in the professional organization. Each nurse also has a responsibility to encourage and promote the membership and participation of others in the organization. Nurses in administrative and teaching positions recognize their unique opportunities for assuming leadership by word and deed in pointing up these responsibilities.

There are various groups with contributions to make in the health field, and in addition to membership in the professional organization, each nurse may wish to support other organizations concerned with health and nursing care.

7. The nurse participates responsibly in defining and upholding standards of professional practice and education.

This statement is representative of a felt need of the profession, for it was included in the 1960 revision of the *Code* by direct request of the ANA House of Delegates which asked that the following concept be incorporated:

>Every professional nurse has an ethical and professional duty, not only to give the best nursing care possible, but also to maintain the standards of the profession so that others elsewhere and in the future may also have adequate nursing care.

Individual performance in nursing forms the base on which the profession as a whole must rest, and each practitioner must set and maintain high individual standards. *The Code for Professional Nurses,* in pointing out responsibility both for self and others, expresses the professional ideal of self-discipline and obligation to others.

To fulfill professional obligations, individual practitioners must participate in defining and upholding standards of professional practice and education. "Defining" standards refers to such activities as work on statements of functions, standards, and qualifications for practice in the vari-

---

* Merton, Robert K. "Functions of the Professional Association," *American Journal of Nursing,* 58:50 (January 1958).

ous areas of nursing, participation in activities relating to curriculum planning, or helping to set standards for accreditation of schools. Individual nurses who do not participate directly in such activities may not feel responsibility for them. Yet they do have reason for concern about any activity relating to standards of practice and education, and should use their voices in their professional organization to make their ideas heard. "Upholding" standards implies a recognition that to grow and progress the profession cannot rest, but must dedicate itself to forward movement through increasingly high standards of care. Each nurse participates in this forward movement by attention to standards of care in the individual work situation.

Educators can greatly influence attitudes toward individual responsibility for standards. Nurses who hold positions as employers, or supervisors of other nurses also have a particular role to play in the enforcement of standards in carrying out their administrative responsibilities. By participating in the development of standards, keeping up to date on changes in standards, providing for the implementation of standards within the institution or agency, bringing standards to the attention of staff, and taking immediate corrective measures when standards are violated, they do much to insure a high level of professional practice.

Inherent in this statement of the *Code* is the responsibility of the profession itself, through its own members, to determine and administer its own standards. The profession is best able to determine what the components of good practice are and also how best its practitioners should be prepared. Consumers of nursing service or related professional disciplines may have much to offer in an advisory capacity. The ultimate responsibility for standards of both education and practice lies within the profession.

8. The nurse maintains professional competence and demonstrates concern for the competence of other members of the nursing profession.

This statement of the *Code* is very closely related to the preceding one in that upholding standards of the profession implies concern for competence of self and others in the profession. It points up the ethical responsibility of the individual practitioner for her own practice and for doing all possible to insure that patients receive the highest quality care from others.

> . . . in the professions, each practitioner *is* his brother's keeper. Each is expected to live up to or to exceed the acceptable standards of practice, and to see that others also do so.*

Nursing differs from most other professions in that the incompetence

---

* *Ibid.*

of a practitioner could result in the loss of health or even the life of a patient. It is therefore especially important that the nurse be prepared adequately for proficient practice and that competence is maintained throughout her professional life.

The dynamic nature of today's civilization with its many scientific advances, amazing discoveries, and new techniques has implications for every nurse. To keep abreast of developments in the nursing field, the practitioner must be alert to opportunities for maintaining and increasing efficiency. Inservice education, short courses of study, conferences, workshops, advanced academic work, professional reading, observation, and investigation are avenues open to nurses. Not only must individual nurses take advantage of them, but part of their professional obligation makes it essential that they work to provide such opportunities for all nurses.

Professional education is a life-long process, and *The Code for Professional Nurses* rightly gives it a place among the obligations of the individual nurse to self and to others in the profession.

9. The nurse assumes responsibility for individual professional actions and judgment, both in dependent and independent nursing functions, and knows and upholds the laws which affect the practice of nursing.

Court cases have amply demonstrated that nurses are held responsible for their own application of expert knowledge. They cannot abrogate responsibility because they follow the physician's order or are employed in an insured hospital or health agency.

Because of ethical responsibility to the public and the legal framework within which the practice of nursing is regulated, nurses should have a working knowledge of the nursing practice laws of any state in which they work. Each nurse must be licensed in the state in which she is currently practicing. No nurse should assume that registration in one state provides the legal basis for practice in any other state. Nurse employers should likewise be concerned for the status of licensure of each staff member, and should require evidence of current credentials upon employment and at periodic intervals thereafter.

Nursing functions may be spelled out to some extent in nursing practice laws. In most states, however, legal definitions of nursing are given in broad terms. Nurses must study the laws and know how their provisions actually apply to individual nursing practice. They should consider their own activities and remember that under the law the nurse, and the nurse alone, is legally accountable for acts which are based on nursing knowledge and judgment as it relates to safe nursing care.

Nursing functions carried out under the direction of a physician are defined as dependent nursing functions, but the nurse must have and utilize for the patient's benefit knowledge of the cause and effect of the orders which she implements. Those functions carried out without a physician's orders are independent nursing functions. Because the number and variety of independent functions in nursing has increased with the changing status of the profession, nurses have assumed increasing responsibility for the effects of their practice. Public accountability is the price of the increased public trust which has come with increased independence.

10. The nurse, acting through the professional organization, participates responsibly in establishing terms and conditions of employment.

This statement of the *Code*, like number seven, was included in the 1960 revision by request of the ANA House of Delegates. The action of the House of Delegates indicates the feeling in the profession that concerted action by the professional organization in the field of economic security is appropriate and necessary if the profession is to discharge its responsibility to the public.

The statement expresses the commitment of the profession to the principle of collective bargaining and its unequivocal acceptance by the House of Delegates indicates that as a professional group, nurses find collective bargaining not only acceptable, but a part of the responsibility of members of the profession. Gillingham* pointed out very clearly that the effective application of high standards and ideals in the daily nursing routine depends upon favorable employment conditions—conditions which nurses themselves have helped to establish. The standards, dignity, and status of nursing cannot be maintained unless economic and personal considerations are congruent with nursing functions and responsibilities. The nursing needs of the nation cannot be met without adequate economic motivation for new recruits to enter the profession.

The responsibilities nurses have assumed and which are stated throughout the *Code* cannot be effectively implemented without participation by nurses in the establishment of terms and conditions of employment. "Terms and conditions of employment" include not only salaries but such factors as opportunity for inservice education and other means of professional growth, provision for health maintenance and, in fact, the very assurance itself that nurses will have the right to participate in establishing appropriate employment conditions. With the right to participate in collective bargaining goes the responsibility for nurses to abide by the terms and conditions of employment which they accept.

Fulfillment of the ethical responsibility set forth in this statement of

---

* Gillingham, J. B., "Collective Bargaining and Professional Ethics," *American Journal of Nursing*, 50:214 (April 1950).

the *Code* can bring significant contributions to better patient care through improved employment conditions for nurses.

11. The nurse has the responsibility to participate in study of and action on matters of legislation affecting nurses and nursing service to the public.

As a professional person, the nurse is expected to take special interest in any legislation—pending, passed, or about to be rescinded—which affects nurses and nursing service to the public. It may be federal, state, or local, and pertain to health needs in general, to social or economic legislation, to medical or nursing practice, or to nursing service given by nonprofessional personnel. In each instance the nurse maintains an alertness to its implications and works with colleagues to effect results which will enable every nurse to give better nursing care. In the area of nursing, the professional nurse is the expert, and thus has a distinctive responsibility to participate in the establishment of standards of nursing practice, uphold them, and assist in their enforcement.

12. The nurse adheres to standards of personal ethics which reflect credit upon the profession.

A characteristic of a profession is its insistence upon high moral standards. It often requires more of the practitioner than the community does. On the member of a profession is imposed the obligation to be cognizant of the public interest and to uphold the dignity of the individual and the brotherhood of man.

The image of nursing is presented to the public primarily through the behavior of its members as practitioners. As it is seldom possible for practitioners to completely divest themselves of professional identification in their private lives, however, the choice of nursing as a career carries with it the responsibility for individual conduct in accord with the ideals of the profession.

13. The nurse may contribute to research in relation to a commercial product or service, but does not lend professional status to advertising, promotion, or sales.

Every nurse should be cognizant of the trust and confidence invested in the profession by the public, and the very great responsibility this imposes on each practitioner. The individual nurse often represents the entire profession to patients and others, and what one nurse says or does may be interpreted as a judgment of the profession, or indicative of a standard by which it abides. Sometimes a symbol of the profession, such as a cap, a pin, or the title may convey the same implication of professional acceptance in certain situations.

The prestige accorded the nursing profession belongs to no one individual nurse, but is the result of the concern and activity of many nurses over a long number of years, working together to establish and constantly improve standards of professional nursing care for the public good. The right to use the title "Registered Nurse" is granted by state governments through licensure by examination for the protection of the public, not for the personal benefit of the nurse or those who may seek to exploit the title for other purposes. Use of the title carries with it the responsibility to act in the public interest, and a license may be revoked for failure to do so.

Advertising and the promotion of products or services occupy a place in our culture and are accepted as recognized business practices. The need for a governmental body, the Federal Trade Commission, to have as one of its functions the investigation of improper advertising practices under-scores the fact, however, that some advertising may be false, misleading, or harmful.

Most advertisers are constantly seeking new and interesting ways of presenting their wares, and some find the picture of a nurse or other symbols of the profession exactly the ingredient needed to give the im-pression of professional concern and scientific protection. The nurse, therefore, is subject to offers to appear in commercial advertising in tele-vision, radio, and the press. Few members of other professions are willing to bring upon themselves the displeasure of their peers by engaging in this type of endeavor, and the truly professional nurse, likewise, refuses to do so.

Competition and commercialism, normal parts of business trans-actions, cannot be associated with the members of a profession without diminishing the usefulness and lowering the dignity of the profession as a whole. An ethical member of the profession not only refuses to participate in questionable activities in relation to commercial products or services, but is concerned and takes appropriate action if other nurses negate their professional responsibility for personal gain.

In the continuing efforts to provide better health care for the public, each nurse should use the various means of communication in such man-ner as will preserve the high standards and best interests of the profession. Reporting the results of research or properly controlled studies through suitable channels is encouraged. Such channels include publications and official meetings for nurses and other groups in the health professions.

In upholding the standards of conduct established by the profession and set forth in *The Code for Professional Nurses,* nurses can help to insure that the skills, symbols, and prestige of their chosen profession are used in the most appropriate and beneficial ways.

14. Nurses, or groups of nurses, who advertise professional services, do so in conformity with the dignity of the nursing profession.

The public has need for information about the various types of professional services available in the community. One means by which the nurse may make known the type of service she is prepared to render is through advertising. Properly used, advertising may prove of benefit to the patient in securing needed care. It is expected, however, that the nurse will limit use of advertising to suitable information presented in a manner consistent with the dignity of the profession and in keeping with the general practices of other professional groups within the community.

Advertising practices recognized as professionally acceptable include the printing of appropriate cards, announcements, and letterheads, and making announcements in telephone directories, magazines, or newspapers. Name, address, title, types of service, hours available, and similar pertinent information may be given. Exaggerated type and style of lettering and format should be avoided as should self-praise and implication of personal superiority over one's colleagues.

Nurses who advertise professional services do so only to the extent needed to help secure and improve the health of the community. They use care in selecting the medium to be used and the details of the announcement to be made.

15. The nurse has an obligation to protect the public by not delegating to a person less qualified any service which requires the professional competence of a nurse.

The professional nurse has responsibility for supervising and guiding less qualified personnel in performing those functions for which they are prepared. The increasing number of team members providing nursing care and nursing service continuously extends this responsibility. In delegating activities to nursing students, practical nurses, nurses' aides, or other nursing service personnel, the professional nurse must evaluate the nursing needs of the patient in relation to the skills and ability level of each team member. The nurse must also be cognizant of both state law and agency policy.

The professional nurse should personally execute those nursing procedures in patient care which require the judgment and competence of the professional practitioner whether these be in the area of physical care, emotional support, teaching, or communication. Concern for the safety and well-being of the patient is the primary consideration of the nurse in making these decisions.

16. The nurse works harmoniously with, and sustains confidence in nursing associates, the physician, and other members of the health team.

Harmonious relationships with professional associates and other members of the health team contribute significantly to the basic aims of nursing care. The nurse gives support and cooperation to co-workers and the employing agency, and maintains these relationships with integrity and discretion.

Harmonious relationships help to create a pleasant work situation and a relaxed and comfortable environment for the patient. They reinforce the patient's confidence in the care he is receiving, and influence his outlook about his illness. Respect for co-workers as individuals and for their contributions to the health team is essential to sustaining confidence in their work.

17. The nurse refuses to participate in unethical procedures and assumes the responsibility to expose incompetence or unethical conduct in others to the appropriate authority.

While the nurse has a responsibility to sustain confidence in co-workers, her primary responsibility is to the public and the patient. In discharging this responsibility, the nurse is concerned not only for her own competence and ethical conduct, but for that of others giving health services.

Basic to professional practice is an understanding of the laws and policies relating to malpractice, unethical conduct, and incompetence. A nurse unknowingly involved in assisting with an unethical procedure, would not be justified in withdrawing at a time when such action might be dangerous to the patient. The nurse should, however, immediately make known objections to the situation and give only such minimum assistance as is necessary.

When a nurse is aware of incompetent, unethical, or illegal practice among co-workers, whether nursing or nonnursing personnel, concern for the care and safety of the patient requires that such practice be reported to the appropriate authority. The most immediate attention to a situation can usually be obtained through the employing agency. The avenue for reporting through the professional association is the committee on nursing practice of the state nurses association. Illegal practice may be reported through this committee or directly to the state board of nursing. Some situations may warrant the concern of all these groups. Reporting should always be objective and based on fact.

Appendix C

MEDICAL DIRECTIVES FOR OCCUPATIONAL HEALTH NURSES*

INTRODUCTION

This statement has been designed to assist in developing medical directives which outline procedures to be used by occupational health nurses. It should be of help to the plant physician, especially to the physician not employed as a full-time medical director, who is required to provide the medical direction for an occupational health program. Written directives and company medical policy provide the occupational health nurse with sound bases for carrying out the objectives of the program.

Since nursing is practiced in health services for workers in commercial and service establishments as well as in industry, the term, "Occupational Health Nurse" is used throughout this report, although "Industrial Nurse" is widely used.

This is not a guide for the development of occupational health programs, but a few introductory words here should be of value to the physician and the occupational health nurse in understanding such programs better and to aid them in the development of written directives. A more complete description of the philosophy and practice of occupational health services can be found in the American Medical Association's "Scope, Objectives, and Functions of Occupational Health Programs."

An occupational health program should provide a positive health maintenance service for employees. This can be accomplished through the application of preventive measures designed to provide a safe and healthful work environment; medical services as required for emergency treatment of the ill or injured; supervision of the health status of the individual

* Publication of the American Medical Association Council on Occupational Health. *Reprinted from the Archives of Environmental Health, December 1962, Vol. 5, pp. 631-637. Copyright 1962, by American Medical Association.* This revision of a 1955 statement entitled, "Guiding Principles and Procedures for Industrial Nurses," was prepared with the advice and assistance of Council member R. Lomax Wells, M.D., and the following consultants: Miss Mary Louise Brown, R.N.; Miss Gertrude A. Stewart, R.N.; Miss Sara P. Wagner, R.N., and Miss Mabel C. Zachary, R.N. and was approved for publication by the Council on Occupational Health.

through examination; counseling and proper job placement; health education; observance of laws and health regulations, and similar services designed to maintain and improve the health and well-being of the worker.

An effective occupational health program may require the services and skills of many professional people, including the physician, the nurse, the industrial hygienist, the sanitary engineer, the safety engineer, and other specially trained persons. Working as a health team with a common objective, these specialists usually can make the work environment safer than that which most employees encounter off the job.

The physician is essential to the proper conduct of an occupational health program, and to him belongs the responsibility for its over-all direction. Although he is the only person qualified to correlate and interpret all of the facts relating to the worker and his individual health, he must rely upon the assistance of other professional persons, one of the most important of whom is the nurse.

The value of the occupational health nurse in the fulfillment of the objectives of an occupational health program is attested by the phenomenal growth of this branch of nursing. The occupational health nurse works with the physician in the plant and is his representative when he is away. She occupies the very strategic position of maintaining closer personal relationships with the employees than do most of her co-workers on the health team. To most of the employees she is often the only visible representative of the in-plant health and medical service. This is not unusual, because the vast majority of occupational health nurses are engaged in single nurse health services, with the physician on an on-call or part-time basis. That hers is a position of serious responsibility is unquestioned, and it is one that produces its own difficulties peculiar to industry.

It is desirable for the occupational health nurse to have special qualifications. The duties and relationships require careful, tactful discharge of nursing functions, while avoiding activities or responsibilities which encroach upon the practice of medicine.

This guide, therefore, sets forth suggestions for:

1. Qualifications, functions, responsibilities, and relationships of occupational health nurses.

2. Medical directives for nursing care in industrial practice.

Numerous references were consulted in the preparation of this guide. A special note of appreciation is extended to the American Association of Industrial Nurses and the Occupational Health Nurses Section of the American Nurses' Association for excellent source material regarding qualifications, functions, relationships, and standard procedures.

SECTION I. QUALIFICATIONS, FUNCTIONS, RELATIONSHIPS, AND RESPONSIBILITIES

QUALIFICATIONS. The occupational health nurse should be a graduate of an accredited school of nursing, registered, and legally qualified to practice within the state where employed. She should be a person with good health, emotional stability, initiative, resourcefulness, sound judgment, and a sincere interest in people. It is essential that she possess thorough knowledge and skills in nursing principles and techniques.

Experience in professional nursing in an occupational health medical department, a public health agency, or the outpatient or emergency department of a hospital, and completion of special courses related to occupational health nursing are highly desirable. Additional attributes include some knowledge of workmen's compensation laws and insurance, health and safety laws, occupational diseases, sanitation, counseling techniques, communication skills, teaching methods, record keeping, and business practices.

In addition to the skills and experience associated with nursing, the occupational health nurse often will find considerable need for training in emergency first aid. The basic training offered by the American Red Cross is excellent. It is recommended that occupational health nurses qualify as first aid instructors so that they may conduct or assist in training classes for the workers in their industry.

When the nurse works under continuous nursing supervision there is less occasion for her to act upon her own initiative, and there may be less need for prior special training and experience.

FUNCTIONS. The functions of the occupational health nurse will depend upon the policy of management, the extent of the occupational health services, and the composition and size of the professional staff. Where the nurse is the only person devoting full time to the health service, her functions may be any or all of the following:

> A. Developing a nursing program to meet the needs of the company's medical policy.
> B. Maintaining the health service facilities, supplies, and equipment.
> C. Providing nursing care for on-the-job employee illnesses and injuries as authorized by the physician-in-charge.
> D. Assisting the physician with the health maintenance of employees, including examinations, in such a manner as has been directed and approved by him.
> E. Developing and maintaining cooperative relations with community physicians and health and welfare agencies.

F. Participating in company safety, sanitation, and welfare activities.

G. Promoting health education and engaging in health counseling.

H. Developing and maintaining adequate records and reports of all services rendered. (However, the nurse should not be so burdened with clerical duties that they interfere with proper performance of her nursing functions.)

I. Maintaining familiarity with the work environment and its hazards through periodic plant tours.

J. Evaluating her own job performance and that of other health service personnel under her supervision.

K. Evaluating periodically the effectiveness of the nursing service and making recommendations for improvement to the physician-in-charge and/or management.

RELATIONSHIPS. 1. Physician in Charge: Legal and ethical considerations require that a physician be given the responsibility for the direction of services relating directly to the health of employees. When services of a full-time medical director are not feasible, management should adopt a physician-in-charge arrangement on a part-time basis. This direction should be active, not passive; personal, not delegated; and definite, even if it consists only of periodic consultation with the nurse relative to routine nursing matters and on-call availability for those situations requiring a physician's service. For her guidance during the physician's absence, the nurse should be provided with medical directives which have been discussed and agreed upon in consultation with her. These should be in writing and signed by the physician-in-charge.

2. Management: The occupational health nurse should report directly to the full-time physician or medical director. When the staff is sufficiently large, the nurse supervisor would report to the physician, and the other nurses on the staff would report to her. When a part-time or other physician-in-charge arrangement has been established, the nurse should report to the physician in all professional matters and to a member of management on administrative matters. The physician ordinarily will represent the health service in conferences with management; however, in the case of a part-time medical service, provision should be made for the nurse to discuss certain nursing problems with management so that they may be resolved promptly and effectively. Management should be conversant with the scope and limitations involved in the practice of nursing, and with the proper medical scope of occupational health service, as outlined in the previously mentioned "Scope, Objectives, and Functions of Occupational Health Programs." Management should neither expect nor request the nurse to exceed her normal sphere of service, nor should the nurse accede to any such expectations or requests.

3. Employees: The occupational health nurse must at all times maintain a confidential professional relationship with the employees, in conformity with legal and ethical codes. A friendly relationship should be established and maintained with employees and employee organizations; however, a position of neutrality is essential whenever matters of conflict with management arise. The nurse is in a key position to promote understanding and appreciation of the benefits of the health service to employees.

Except where law dictates otherwise, the nurse should never divulge information in the individual employee health records unless the employee gives his signed permission. These records are always to be considered confidential and should be filed in the health service department, accessible only to medical department personnel.

4. Community Physicians: The nurse should exercise discretion in the handling of nonoccupational ailments, and this must be in accord with directives of the physician-in-charge, followed by referral of the employee, when indicated, to his personal physician for further treatment. When the employee has no personal physician and requests referral to one, the nurse should request the physician-in-charge to make recommendations or provide a referral list.

5. Community Services: The occupational health nurse should be familiar with the various official and voluntary health and welfare agencies in the community. Cooperative relationships should be developed and maintained so that proper referrals can be made as the need arises.

6. Professional Nursing Organizations: It is desirable for the occupational health nurse to maintain membership in local and national organizations devoted to professional nursing, to attend meetings, and to participate in special courses and other educational activities in order to keep abreast of the latest developments in the field of medical and nursing sciences.

RESPONSIBILITIES. Certain basic principles apply in delineating the responsibilities, prerogatives, and limitations involved in the physician-nurse relationship in industry. The establishment of a medical diagnosis and the definition of treatment are the function of the physician.

It is the physician's responsibility to define procedures for the care of illness or injury and the nurse's responsibility to carry them out. The nurse should not be called upon to give service or to make decisions upon professional matters that do not fall within the field of her training and licensure.

The nurse must follow the medical directives prepared for her guidance by the physician-in-charge. Such directives should embrace the types of minor injuries and ailments that might be incurred by the employees in the industry, and specify the kind of first aid or other treatment to be given, with the physician-in-charge available on call. Such directives are not intended to be a substitute for physician care or to give the occupational health nurse permission to practice medicine but are a realistic recognition of the fact that proper and careful attention by a professional nurse, with a physician available when needed, is much more to be desired than the common practice of self-medication or neglect of minor injuries and ailments when occupational health services are not available. In cases of sudden serious illness or injury, however, the nurse should take such measures as the situation demands until a physician has relieved her of further responsibility.

Legal Principles: Management, physician, and nurse should be familiar with the laws regulating the practice of medicine and nursing in their states and also with professional liability and malpractice insurance coverages and limitations.

It is difficult to make a clear-cut distinction between those acts which must be performed by a licensed physician and those which may be delegated to a nurse. One primary rule is that a physician may not properly delegate to a nonphysician the performance of any function requiring the exercise of professional medical judgment. However, according to "The Legal Scope of Industrial Nursing Practice," a statement published by the American Medical Association in 1959,

> Courts have held that professional nurses have a legal duty to interpret evidence presented by the patient possibly indicating the need for medical attention, and to proceed in the light of that interpretation to do what is required for the patient, as for example the need to call a physician; to discontinue a treatment where there is evidence of its harmful effect, e.g., on an unconscious patient; or to determine the patient's need for special medication, e.g., sedatives. There can be little doubt that by custom and usage the relationship between doctor, patient, and nurse is one in which the parties recognize that the nurse as well as the physician has the function and responsibility to observe and interpret the patient's reactions.

It states further that:

> In emergency cases, industrial nurses have a duty to determine the need for prompt medical attention, to make a tentative diagnosis of the patient's condition, and to employ necessary resuscitative and first-aid measures.

The physician is required to exercise professional judgment and discretion in making a diagnosis and prescribing treatment. The nurse, in carrying out the physician's order, is required to exercise professional ability and skill. The nurse must bear in mind at all times that she is required to perform duties assumed by her in a competent manner and that she may be personally responsible for wrongful acts or negligence even if performed under the authority of a physician.

The occupational health nurse should not rely on "standing orders," standing procedures, or medical directives from a physician who has not been designated by management as the physician-in-charge of the occupational health service.

The occupational health nurse must strive constantly to retain the role of nurse and should not accept employment that requires her to assume responsibility for service outside the sphere of her professional training and experience. Management should not employ a nurse without first investigating her qualifications and experience to function as an occupational health nurse.

SECTION II. MEDICAL DIRECTIVES

The occupational health nurse should have written medical directives in order to perform many of her duties. Such directives outline the procedures prescribed by the physician-in-charge to govern her activities in the handling of emergency and routine situations with ill or injured individuals before they are seen by a physician. It cannot be overemphasized that medical directives should be prepared only by the physician-in-charge of the medical service, in consultation with the nurse. They must be in writing, signed by the physician, and revised periodically.

To facilitate the preparation and adoption of medical directives, certain basic suggestions are offered as a guide for the physician.

GENERAL PRINCIPLES FOR EMERGENCY SITUATIONS. The following general principles are applicable to all emergencies.

1. Call a physician immediately.
2. Control bleeding.
3. Restore breathing.
4. Prevent shock and infection.
5. Do no more than is actually needed.

The supervising physician should assure himself that these instructions are thoroughly understood and should institute special training when necessary. The following procedures should apply for specific situations.

Hemorrhage: Excessive bleeding calls for immediate attention. The nurse should notify the physician and, until he arrives, proceed as follows:

1. Expose the wound.
2. Remove loose, surface foreign matter.
3. Apply pressure.

Direct pressure firmly applied over sterile gauze at the bleeding site usually will effectively control moderate hemorrhage. Indirect compression is indicated in excessive bleeding not controllable by direct methods. Digital compression over the vessel against underlying structures either adjacent to the wound or at the nearest pressure point will usually suffice until the physician arrives. Indirect pressure should be applied proximal or distal to the wound, in keeping with the arterial or venous character of the bleeding. Hemostats or clamps should be applied only if the emergency warrants it and when the foregoing procedures prove ineffective. Avoid applying a tourniquet if possible. If severe bleeding in an extremity suggests the use of a tourniquet, apply a blood pressure cuff. The nurse should remember that:

1. A direct pressure bandage should not act as a tourniquet.
2. A tourniquet must be periodically released every 15 minutes.
3. No dressing should be applied over a tourniquet.
4. Sterile precautions must be observed at all times.

Asphyxia: Cessation of breathing from any cause demands:

1. Mouth-to-mouth respiration at once and at the site of the accident.
2. Notification of the physician.
3. Maintenance of body warmth, but avoid excessive heating.

All occupational health nurses should possess the ability to apply mouth-to-mouth respiration and should realize the need for its continuous application until breathing is restored or until careful, repeated medical examination advises otherwise.

Shock: Early and adequate shock treatment is life saving. Do not delay. Common symptoms of shock following injury are pallor, perspiration, and rapid thready pulse. Emergency management by the nurse should include the following procedures:

1. Notify the physician.
2. Remove the cause. If shock is due to hemorrhage, control it. If it is due to trauma not associated with bleeding, all active treatment of injury should be deferred until shock management has been instituted. Wounds should be covered with sterile dressings to prevent infection.
3. Relieve the pain. Medication as ordered by the physician by telephone or written order. Telephone orders should be written on the patient's chart, and the physician should sign them after he has given the employee all other emergency care indicated.
4. Keep the patient warm, dry, and on his back with his head low.

Unconsciousness: 1. Fainting. Usually signs are pallor, shallow breathing, and slow and weak pulse; periods of unconsciousness are of short duration. Keep the patient lying down with head lowered until fully recovered. Be sure patient has plenty of fresh air. Clothing should be loosened and stimulating inhalants used such as ammonia or smelling salts.

2. Other Causes. If other signs are present or if unconsciousness persists longer than a few minutes, call for medical assistance. Give nothing by mouth.

Eye Injuries: No patient with an eye injury should be discharged without examination by a physician. The greatest care must be exercised in maintaining the sterility of solutions and medications for use in the eye. These should be changed frequently. Consecutive patients should never be attended without sterilization of instruments and careful hand washing before and after treatment. Early symptoms of infection, it must be remembered, can simulate a foreign body. Specific procedures should be written for the following: foreign body in the eye, conjunctivitis, minor burns, chemical burns, hot metal burns, "flash injury."

Other Injuries: Other injuries are likely to be encountered in industry, and the physician-in-charge should supply the nurse with written signed procedures for her guidance. Additions may be made to this list by the physician-in-charge in keeping with the needs as defined by him or the nurse. The minimum list is as follows: abrasions, contusions, lacerations, puncture wounds, slivers and splinters, burns and scalds, chemical burns, sprains and strains, fractures, head injuries, chest and abdominal injuries.

PROCEDURES FOR COMPLAINTS OF A NONEMERGENCY NATURE. Dermatitis: Most skin disease occurring in industrial employment are true contact dermatoses; however, not all eruptions arising in workers result from his employment. Many cases are caused by substances contacted outside of working hours. In cases of skin disease that are suspicious of being contact in origin, arrangements should be made for prompt examination by the physician.

The treatment of nonoccupational skin disease is not the function of an occupational health department. Any therapy by the nurse of occupationally incurred skin disease and injuries should be limited to the carrying out of instruction by the physician.

Minor skin injuries should be treated promptly and adequately to prevent subsequent infection. The use of sulfonamides, penicillin, and the local anesthetics should be avoided in order to prevent contact dermatitis produced by overzealous treatment.

The alleviation of itching, burning, and redness should be exercised only by the use of soothing applications. Proprietary compounds should be avoided except for those recommended by the attending physician or dermatologist. A dermatological consultant or an experienced industrial physician should be consulted in the selection of stock therapeutic materials to be applied to the skin.

Other Complaints: The following complaints are most commonly encountered in industry, and the physician-in-charge should provide the nurse with written and signed procedures for each complaint: fever, headache, earache, toothache, nose bleed, sore throat, respiratory infections; abdominal distress, nausea, or pain; dysmenorrhea. In addition, medical directives should be provided for pregnancy, heart attacks, electric shock, epileptic seizures, heat cramps, heat exhaustion, and heat stroke or sun stroke.

Persistent or recurring symptoms or irritation, discomfort, or disability may suggest faulty work environment. The nurse should not hesitate to request medical examination of employees and inspection of the work location by appropriate authorities.

Council on Occupational Health, American Medical Association, 535 N. Dearborn St., Chicago 10, Ill.

SUGGESTED READING LIST

Scope, Objectives and Functions of Occupational Health Programs
The Legal Scope of Industrial Nursing Practice
Expired Air Resuscitation in Industry
Guiding Principles and Procedures for Industrial Nurses in the Care of Eye Injuries
Occupational Health Services for Women Employees
Guide to Development of an Industrial Medical Records System
Obtain from:
   American Medical Association, Council on Occupational Health, 535 N. Dearborn St., Chicago 10, Ill.

Objectives of an Industrial Nursing Service
Principles of Management-Nurse Relationship in Industry
Principles of Physician-Nurse Relationship in Industry
Recommended Job Responsibilities (Consultant, Administrator of a Health Service, Administrator of Nursing Services, Charge Nurse, Staff Nurse, Supervisor, Junior Supervisor, Visiting Nurse)
Principles of Privileged Communications
The Principles of Record Keeping
Guide for the Preparation of a Manual of Policies and Procedures for the Professional Nurse in Industry
Guide to Interviewing and Counseling for the Professional Nurse in Industry

Obtain from:

    American Association of Industrial Nurses, Inc., 170 E. 61st St., New York 21, N.Y.

Functions, Standards, and Qualifications for Occupational Health Nurses (1960 Revision)

The Nurse in Small Industry

Glossary

The Legal Scope of Occupational Health Nursing, by Grace C. Barbee

The Role of the Occupational Health Nurse (Eye Care)

Obtain from:

    American Nurses Association, 10 Columbus Circle, New York 19, N.Y.

Index